KU-566-969

Cellular Radio

Principles and Design

R. C. V. Macario

Department of Electronic and Electrical Engineering
University of Wales, Swansea

Second Edition

© R. C. V. Macario 1993, 1997

All rights reserved. No reproduction, copy or transmission of
this publication may be made without written permission.

No paragraph of this publication may be reproduced, copied or
transmitted save with written permission or in accordance with
the provisions of the Copyright, Designs and Patents Act 1988,
or under the terms of any licence permitting limited copying
issued by the Copyright Licensing Agency, 90 Tottenham Court
Road, London W1P 9HE.

Any person who does any unauthorised act in relation to this
publication may be liable to criminal prosecution and civil
claims for damages.

The author has asserted his right to be identified
as the author of this work in accordance with the
Copyright, Designs and Patents Act 1988.

First edition 1993
Second edition 1997

Published by
MACMILLAN PRESS LTD
Houndmills, Basingstoke, Hampshire RG21 6XS
and London
Companies and representatives
throughout the world

ISBN 0–333–69153–9

A catalogue record for this book is available
from the British Library.

This book is printed on paper suitable for recycling and
made from fully managed and sustained forest sources.

10 9   8   7   6   5   4   3   2   1
06 05 04 03 02 01 00 99 98 97

Printed and bound in Great Britain by
Antony Rowe Ltd, Chippenham, Wiltshire

621.3845
MAC

Contents

Appendices

Preface to the Second Edition

This book is designed to appeal to any student of the technology and operation of cellular radio, whether at advanced undergraduate or postgraduate level, or undertaking a further training course, or at practitioner level. It is assumed that the reader has a basic knowledge of electronic engineering, together with some experience in quantitative evaluation. The aims are to provide such readers with an understanding and appreciation of one of the fastest growing socially apparent artifacts in engineering today.

It has been said that there are some 30,000 subscribers being added to digital cellular networks alone every day. An operator who would have had to instal, say, a few hundred base stations for a national analog network, is now looking at having to instal a thousand and more base stations for *partial* national digital cellular coverage. The diagram below illustrates the dilemma of the author. The first edition was started at the zero digital projection point; at the time of writing one appears to be at the maximum of a take-off phase.

UK Digital Growth Projections

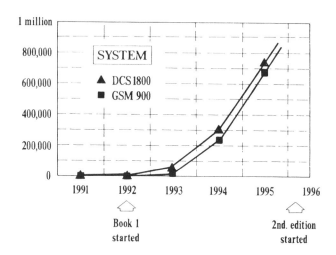

By having an annotated map of the world beside his desk the author can keep in view the reality of the various world cellular systems. The book is therefore carefully balanced to give equal weight to all systems; for example, AMPS/D-AMPS in the Americas, GSM/DCS 1800 in other parts of the world.

The material included is drawn from experience gained in teaching courses on cellular communications to various classes, over many years, as well as from practical experience in designing, evaluating and operating cellular and other equipment.

Having spent much of his career in the field of radio communication, the author readily acknowledges the contribution made over the years to his teaching and research by data and information disseminated through seminars and similar events, especially those held by the leading manufacturers of test equipment, for the design and evaluation of radio equipment and cellular. In particular, he wishes to acknowledge the Hewlett Packard Company, Marconi Instruments Ltd and Rohde & Schwarz UK Ltd.

The writer has also had the advantage of being conversant with all the major UK operators, i.e. Cellnet, One-2-One, Orange and Vodafone, as well as the internationally renowned infrastructure and handset suppliers. He trusts that he has kept good faith with all concerned.

Once again I wish to thank Angela McGairl of the Engineering Faculty of the University of Wales, Swansea for preparing the drawings; Ruth Baker for preparing the text; and Malcolm Stewart of the Macmillan Press for his help and encouragement. I am also grateful to my family for accepting that the book took precedence at home and at weekends for a long time. I am especially grateful to my wife, Margaret, for her continual support and encouragement

R.C.V. Macario

Abbreviations and Acronyms Associated with Cellular Radio

A	*An interface*
A3, A5	*Cipher codes*
AB	*Access Burst*
ACCH	*Associated Control Channel*
ACS	*Adjacent Channel/Carrier Suppression*
ACI	*Adjacent Channel Interference*
ACU	*Antenna Combination Unit*
ADC	*American Digital Cellular*
ADM	*Adaptive Delta Modulation*
ADPCM	*Adaptive PCM*
AFC	*Automatic Frequency Control*
AGC	*Automatic Gain Control*
AGCH	*Access Grant Channel*
AGWN	*Additive White Guassian Noise*
AI	*Area Identification (field)*
AMPS	*Automatic Mobile Phone Service (USA)*
APC	*Airborne Public Correspondence*
ARFCH	*Absolute Radio Frequency Channel*
ARQ	*Automatic Request for Re-transmission*
ATM	*Asynchronous Transfer Mode*
AUC	*Authentication Centre*
Au	*Authentication*
BCC	*Base (station) Colour Code*
BCCH	*Broadcast Control Channel*
BCH	*Broadcast Channel*
BCH	*Bose-Chaudhuri-Hocquenghem code*
BER	*Bit Error Rate*
B$_m$	*Traffic channel for full-rate voice coder (ISDN terminology for mobile service)*
BP	*Bit periods*
BS	*Base Station*
BSC	*Base Station Controller*
BSCU	*Base Station Controller Unit*
BSI	*Base Station Interface*

BSIC	*Base Station Identity Code*
BSS	*Base Station System*
BSSAP	*Base Station Application Part*
BTS	*Base Transceiver Station*
CA	*Cell Allocation*
CA-CN	*Cell Allocation RF Channel Number*
CBCH	*Cell Broadcast Channel*
CC	*Country Code*
CCCH	*Common Control Channel*
CCIR	*Consultative Committee for International Radiocommunications*
CDMA	*Code Division Multiple Access*
CDVCC	*Coded Digital Verificaiton Colour Code*
CELP	*Code Excited Linear Predictor*
CFEK	*Coherent Frequency Shift Keying*
CGI	*Cell Global Identity*
CCITT	*International Telegraph and Telephone Consultative Committee*
CI	*Cell Identity*
CPA	*Combined Paging Access (field)*
CPFSK	*Continuous Phase Frequency Shift Keying*
CRC	*Cyclic Redundancy Check*
CSPDN	*Circuit Switched Public Data Network*
CU	*Central Unit (of a MS)*
C/I	*Carrier-to-Interference Ratio*
D	*Downlink*
D/A	*Digital to Analog*
DB	*Dummy Burst*
DCC	*Digital Colour Code*
DCS	*Digital Cellular System*
DCF	*Data Communication Function*
DCCH	*Dedicated Control Channel*
DCN	*Data Communication Network*
DECT	*Digitally Enhanced Cordless Telecommunication*
DL	*Data Link (layer)*
DLD	*Data Link Discriminator*

D$_m$	*Control Channel*
	(ISDN terminology for mobile service)
DMR	*Digital Mobile Radio*
DP	*Dialled Pulse*
DRX	*Discontinuous Reception*
DSP	*Digital Signal Processor*
DTAP	*Direct Transfer Application Part*
DTE	*Data Terminal Equipment*
DTMF	*Dual-Tone Multi-Frequency (signalling)*
DTX	*Discontinuous Transmission (field)*
ECP	*Echo Canceller in pool*
EIA	*Electronic Industry Association*
E$_b$/N$_o$	*Ratio of energy-per-bit to noise power spectral density*
EIR	*Equipment Identity Register*
END	*End Indication (field)*
ESN	*Electronic Serial Number*
E-TACS	*Extended TACS (more channels)*
ETC	*Exchange Terminal Circuit*
ETSI	*European Telecoms Standards Institute*
FB	*Frequency (correction) Burst*
FACCH	*Fast Associated Control Channel*
FCCH	*Frequency Correction Channel*
FDMA	*Frequency Division Multiple Access*
FEC	*Forward Error Correction*
FER	*Frame Erasure Rate*
FCC	*Forward Control Channel*
FN	*Frame Number*
FREG	*Forced Registration (field)*
FSK	*Frequency Shift Keying*
FVC	*Forward Voice Channel*
G	*Guard (bit periods)*
GFSK	*Gaussian Frequency Shift Keying*
GIM	*Group Identification Mark*
GMPCS	*Global Mobile Personal Communications by Satellite*

GMSC	*Gateway Mobile Switching Centre*
GMSK	*Gaussian Minimum Shift Keying*
GOS	*Grade of Service*
GSM	*Global System for Mobile Communications*
	previously: Group Special Mobile
GSM PLMN	*GSM Public Land Mobile Network*
HDLC	*High Level Data Link Control*
HLR	*Home Location Register*
HLRID	*Home Mobile Switching Centre*
HON	*Handover Number*
HPLMN	*Home PLMN*
HPU	*Handportable Unit*
ID	*Identification*
IDN	*Integrated Digital Network*
IMSI	*International Mobile Subscriber Identification*
IS-54	*EIA Interim Standard for U.S. Digital Cellular*
	(USDC)
IS-95	*EIA Interim Standard for U.S. Code Division*
	Multiple Access
IS-136	*EIA Interim Standard 136 - USDC with Digital*
	Control Channels
ISDN	*Integrated Services Digital Network*
ISI	*Intersymbol Interference*
ITU	*International Telecommunications Union*
IWF	*Inter Working Function*
JDC	*Japanese Digital Cellular*
JRC	*Joint Radio Committee*
J-TACS	*Japanese TACS system*
JTC	*Joint Technical Committee*
$\mathbf{K}_i\ \mathbf{K}_c$	*Cipher Keys*
LAC	*Location Area Code*
LAI	*Location Area Identity*
LAN	*Local Area Network*

LAR	*Log-area Ratio*
LE	*Local Exchange*
LMSI	*Local Mobile Station Identificaiton*
LOS	*Line of Sight*
LPC	*Linear Predictive Coding*
LR	*Location Register*
LTP	*Long Term Prediction*
MA	*Mobile Allocation*
MACN	*Mobile Allocation Channel Number*
MAHO	*Mobile Assisted Handover*
MAP	*Mobile Application Part*
MCC	*Mobile Country Code*
ME	*Mobile Equipment*
MIC	*Mobile Interface Controller*
MIN	*Mobile Identification Number*
MMI	*Man Machine Interface*
MNC	*Mobile Network Code*
MOS	*Mean Opinion Score*
MPE	*Multi-Pulse Excitation*
MS	*Mobile Station*
MSC	*Mobile Switching Centre*
MSCU	*Mobile Station Control Unit*
MSIN	*Mobile Station Identification Number*
MSISDN	*Mobile Station ISDN Number*
MSL	*Main Signalling Link*
MSRN	*Mobile Station Roaming Number*
MSS	*Mobile Satellite Services*
NAM	*Number Assignment Module*
N-AMPS	*Narrowband AMPS system*
NB	*Normal Burst*
NCELL	*Neighbouring (adjacent) Cell*
NDC	*Network Destination Code*
NE	*Network Element*
NMC	*Network Management Centre*
NMSI	*National Mobile Station Identification (number)*
NMT	*Nordic Mobile Telephone (system)*

NSAP	*Network Service Access Point*
N(S)N	*National (Significant) Number*
NT	*Network Termination*
OFDM	*Orthogonal Frequency Division Multiplexing*
OHD	*Overhead Message Type Field*
OMC	*Operations & Maintenence Centre*
OQPSK	*Offset Quatrature Phase Shift Keying*
OSI	*Open System Interconnection*
OSS	*Operator Service System*
P	*Parity Field*
PA	*Power Amplifier*
PCH	*Paging Channel*
PCM	*Pulse Code Modulator*
PCN	*Personal Communications Network*
PCS	*Personal Communication Services*
PDN	*Public Data Networks*
PHS	*Personal Handyphone System*
PIN	*Personal Identification Number*
PLMN	*Public Land Mobile Network*
PMR	*Private Mobile Radio*
PN	*Pseudo Noise (code)*
PSK	*Phase Shift Keying*
PSPDN	*Public Switched Public Data Network*
PSTN	*Public Switched Telephone Network*
PTO	*Public Telecommunications Operator*
QOS	*Quality of Service*
QPSK	*Quadrature Phase Shift Keying*
RACH	*Random Access Channel*
RAND	*Random Number*
RCC	*Reverse Control Channel*
REC	*RECommendation*
REGH	*Registration Field for Mobile*
REL	*RELease*
RELP	*Residual Excited Linear Predictive (coder)*

REQ	*REQuest*
RES	*RESponse (authentication)*
RFCH	*Radio Frequency Channel*
RLP	*Radio Link Protocol*
RPE	*Regular Pulse Excitation (Voice Coder)*
RPF	*Radio Fixed Part*
RR	*Radio Resource*
RSE	*Radio System Entity*
RSVD	*Reserved for Future Use (bits)*
RVC	*Reverse Voice Channel*
RX	*Receiver, or R_x*
SACCH	*Slow Associated Control Channel*
SAP	*Service Access Point*
SAPI	*Service Access Point Indicator*
SAT	*Supervisory Audio Tone*
SB	*Synchronization Burst*
SCC	*SAT Colour Code*
SCCP	*Signalling Connection Control Part*
SCH	*Synchronization Channel*
SCM	*Station Class Mark*
SCP	*Service Control Point*
SDCCH	*Stand-alone Dedicated Control CHannel*
SIDH	*System Identification of Home Mobile Service Area*
SIM	*Subscriber Identity Module*
SLTM	*Signalling Link Test Message*
SMS	*Short Message Service*
SN	*Subscriber Number or Serial Number*
SNR	*Signal-to-Noise Ratio*
SP	*Signalling Point*
SRES	*Signed Response*
SS7	*Signalling System No. 7*
ST	*Signalling Tone*
SYNC	*Synchronization Signal*
TA	*Terminal Adaptor*
TACS	*Total Access Communications (UK)*

TB	*Tail Bits*
TC	*Trunk Code*
TCH	*Traffic CHannel*
TDD	*Time Division Duplex*
TDMA	*Time Division Multiple Access*
TE	*Terminal Equipment*
TFM	*Tamed Frequency Modulation*
TFTS	*Terrestrial Flight Telephone System*
TIA	*Telecommunications Industry Association (USA)*
TMN	*Telecommunications Management Network*
TMSI	*Temporary Mobile Subscriber Identification*
TN	*Time slot Number*
TRAU	*Transcoder Unit*
TRX	*Transceiver*
TS	*Training Sequence; also Time Slot*
TSC	*Training Sequence Code*
TU	*Typical Urban (profile)*
TX	*Transmitter, or T_x*
U	*Uplink*
U$_m$	*Air Interface*
VAD	*Voice Activitity Detection*
VCO	*Voltage Controlled Oscillator*
VLR	*Visitor Location Register*
VLSI	*Very Large Silicon Integrated (circuit)*
VMAC	*(Voice) Mobile Attenuation Code*
VSELP	*Vector Sim Excited Linear Predictor*
WAN	*Wide Area Network*
WARC	*World Administrative Conference*
WLAN	*Wireless Local Area Network*

[Note: this list is not necessarily exhaustive]

1 Introduction

Cellular radio is a complex technological system. It embraces several disciplines of engineering and has taken much enterprise and development to assemble into global systems. For example, cellular radio requires the combining of many large scale technologies, such as efficient high frequency semiconductor technology, radio transmission planning and global fixed telecommunications networks. The approach taken in this text, therefore, is firstly to set out an overview of the main disciplines and designs involved. Chapter 1 presents this overview; the varied details of the many 'parts' can then be studied in the chapters which follow.

A particular aspect of cellular radio, as indeed is the case with many other subjects, is the appearance and common use of acronyms. Those generally found in use for cellular radio are listed at the front of the book. They are all abbreviations, for example, MSC – mobile switching centre, and there is a temptation to proceed using these abbreviations freely from then on in the text. This has been avoided where possible, at least in the earlier chapters, so that they can be read more easily. Towards the end of the text, however, so much detail is involved that these acronyms are used more often. By then the first time reader will have come to terms with many of the abbreviations.

Another attribute of cellular radio is that it is a mature technology, even though this maturity has come about in a short time scale; in fact, it is younger than most of the people working in the discipline. The speed of realization is much faster than that of other public domain engineering activities; for example the rail network, the fixed telephone network and motorway networks.

Although it is generally recognized that fixed telecommunications networks (telephones, facsimile, etc.), are the largest and most completely integrated technological systems at present found in the world, cellular radio is fast becoming of equal size and complexity. In analogous terms, one could say that cellular radio is like the sunflower in nature; it begins with quite a small seed, grows with a tree-like stem within one season, produces a brilliant coloured flower, which then turns to face the sun, the source of nutrition (in cellular, the subscriber). The sunflower also produces more of its own kind (seeds) found, one notes, in a cellular arrangement; cellular radio virtually does the same.

1.1 The radiotelephone

A radiotelephone can be defined as a telephone without wires, the connection to the local exchange, however, is now through the medium of *radio*. To achieve

1

this operation many new factors above and beyond the basic telephone must be introduced.

Let us just recall what are the features of the so-called plain old telephone. Figure 1.1 shows these in a semi-descriptive way.

The telephone has a number which is registered solely in the local exchange (LE). Numbers can be dialled from the phone using a keypad, and the accepted dual-tone multi-frequency (DTMF) format, Figure 1.2, is the usual means of transferring these numbers. Electrical power to operate the ringer and other functions in the phone is supplied by the local exchange through the two wires of the *local loop*. Only two wires are used, but these achieve a two-way or duplex mode of conversation. However, the length of the local loop to the exchange is limited, because amplification is not possible both ways with only two wires. As a result, within the fixed telephone network a two-wire to four-wire conversion takes place.

It is perhaps also worth pointing out that the four-wire loop can also lead to 'echoes' on the phone. *Delay* in the network emphasizes any echo, i.e., the talker hears his own voice after a delay. Delay times in digital cellular are especially described in Chapter 7, section 4.

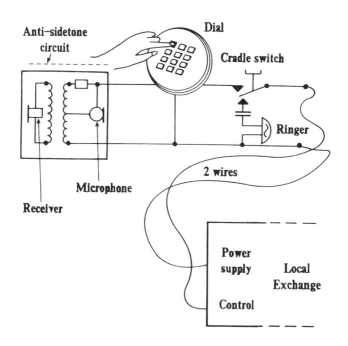

Figure 1.1 The basic telephone with a two-wire connection to the local exchange

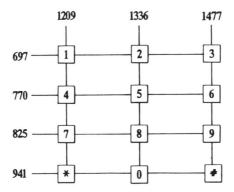

Figure 1.2 The dual-tone multi-frequency keypad and associated audio tones (two out of one-from-four code); shown in Hertz

Another feature is the cradle found on all telephones; this alerts the local exchange as to whether the phone is *on* or *off hook*. Such artifacts, which make the telephone system work, are merely listed at this point in the description as features. These features are paramount within the fixed telephone network system, however.

In what way does the *radiotelephone* (R/T) differ? Again a semi-descriptive diagram is a good place to start and here Figure 1.3 is perhaps helpful. Clearly a radiotelephone differs in many ways.

- An R/T requires a portable source of power – its (rechargeable) battery – in order to function.

- The local exchange is now replaced by a (local) *base station* (BS), which is to be found in Figure 1.6 below, for example. The base station is fixed wire connected within a mobile telephone network usually known as a *public land mobile network (PLMN),* which may be part of, or in addition to, the fixed network mentioned above.

- Both the radiotelephone – now called the *mobile station* (MS) (but we will use the word mobile in general) – and the base station need a radio *antenna.*

- These antennas must be suitable for the radio frequencies which are allocated within the radio spectrum, being those licensed for use by the radio telephones in operation.

- Two radio channels in general must be allocated to each mobile phone in order to have duplex operation, that is, the user can speak and listen at the same time. Variation on this theme using *time division duplex* (TDD) operation is described later, but whatever the case, a *forward* and a *return* path radio channel is required.

The forward channel refers to the base-to-mobile path; the reverse channel refers to the mobile-to-base path. Both the BS and the MS require radio transmitter circuits. The weakest path is the return path, because the mobile unit has limited radio power, in order to conserve battery power and extend operational time between charging (overnight). Cellular radio is designed to overcome this limitation.

• The mobile carries its own telephone number which may be built into the radio as indicated in Figure 1.3, or be part of a removable personalized *smart card*, as internal memory. This is unique to a personal radiotelephone or cellular radio. It allows the subscriber to roam over cellular networks – provided that he can set up agreement with the local base station where he is operating.

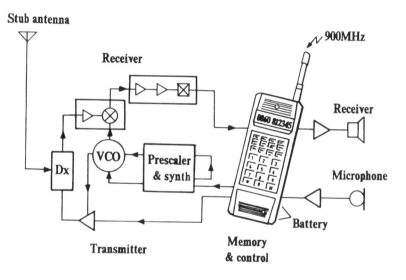

Figure 1.3 Outline of the components within a cellular radiotelephone

• The mobile will also contain a radio receiver, transmitter and tuning (synthesizer) circuits which must be supplied by power from the battery and which take and give instructions to the local memory and control module.

• The ringer is now controlled through the previous circuits. Notice that no cradle is found on a radiotelephone (as opposed to the much simpler cordless telephones which we do not discuss). The BS and MS in fact automatically keep in touch by various handshaking protocols. A call is set up by depressing a specific SEND button (which now generally carries a coloured off-hook sign) on the keyboard, not associated with the DTMF keyboard set.

It is clear that a radio or cellular telephone handset is completely different in technology from a fixed telephone instrument, not just in the fact that the wire to the local exchange is missing. The sets also differ specifically as regards several operational features.

• Provided that a mobile radio telephone network and service has been set up, by the network operator and the holder of the radio licence to run such a service, then the subscriber (to the service, the user of the radiotelephone) can *roam* around the network, or country as he wishes, so long as he stays within radio distance of a base station.

• Our subscriber has a telephone number, now called a mobile telephone number, which is registered to the handset. The number will usually be of the same format as numbers allocated to fixed subscribers, shown in general in Figure 1.4, except that the area or office code will not refer to a specific town or district say, but to a specific mobile telephone service. Also note, whether phoning from a fixed or cellular telephone, a two digit access code determines what service you are seeking, namely

00	–	international call
01/02	–	national fixed call
03/04/07	–	mobile service access

In addition, 08 prefixes call up special, or premium services. (Note, these prefixes may not of course apply to all countries, or at the present time.)

The fixed network of PLMN will hold a register of mobile numbers for billing, authentication and location purposes, but the mobile phone number personal to the handset does of course go hand-in-hand with the roaming feature.

• Finally, for call management, much more sophisticated signalling between the handset and the local base station (and supporting network) is necessary, and specific instructions must be given by the mobile; these instructions are of course usually transparent to the user. Thus a large amount of digital data traffic is found in cellular radio, whether the system is analog or digital.

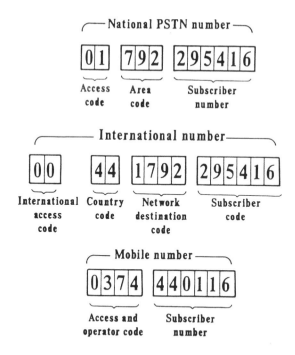

Figure 1.4 The international and national number format in the UK at the present time

1.2 Expanding the number of subscribers

The simple radiotelephone description suggests that the number of phones and hence subscribers could be expanded quite readily by allocating sufficient radio spectrum, i.e. more channels to the radio telephone service and therefore having a large number of duplex traffic radio channels. The shortcomings of this approach are however easily appreciated.

- Firstly, for example, 40 MHz of allocated spectrum really means 20 MHz because of duplex operation. If the equivalent of 20 kHz per channel is achieved, this means that only 1000 users, or less than point one percent of the population in cities of over one million people, would have access to the radio channels at any one time.

- Secondly, the near-far problem of radio range is a real difficulty. How does one manage a subscriber at the edge of the radio range? In such a location his signal would more than likely be suppressed by a user close to his frequency and close to the base station.

- Thirdly, how does one achieve an orderly coverage of a complete state or country and allow a subscriber to roam smoothly through a mobile telephone network only employing a specific number of allocated radio channels?

1.3 The cellular principle

The required step forward is called the cellular principle. Put simply, radio cells, defined by a base station at their centre, are distributed evenly in clusters with an allowed overlap of coverage. Figure 1.5 illustrates the beginnings of such a distribution of cells, when laid out on a nice flat plain.

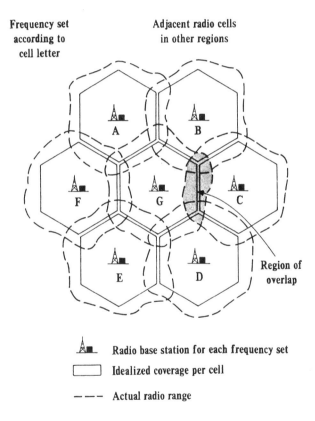

Figure 1.5 The concept of cell distribution and the honeycomb pattern

The first observation, after examining the diagram, is that a different set of frequencies must be used (allocated) to all the adjacent cells around the cell letter G at the centre. The signals here give rise to *adjacent channel* interference, but this can be minimized by control of the radio signal modulation and transmitter/receiver design. However, the same set of frequencies needs to be used at more distant cells outside the diagram.

This is the principle of repeating and the *reuse* of frequencies in the operation. The physical distance from the centre of the centre cell to the repeat cell centre is called the *reuse distance*, D. The cell size is defined by its *radius*, R. The relationships between the terms D and R are discussed in Chapter 3.

An important aspect of the reuse of the same radio channels and frequencies in nearby cells means that cellular radio operation is to a large extent limited by pre-planned *co-channel interference*. The ability of the particular modulation strategy used for signalling and messaging to combat co-channel interference will determine the *cluster size* of the system.

The approach of allowing cell overlap and then, later, repeating the use of the same radio frequencies (channels) is the cellular radio principle.

There is no recognized historical mark as to when the idea was first put forward; to some extent one could say that once the concept of the frequency synthesizer was put forward and demonstrated in the early 1960s the opportunity to have frequency active mobiles came about.

The first practical cellular system to appear was the Japanese AMPS (automatic mobile phone system) in metropolitan Tokyo in 1979, followed closely by the Nordic (NMT 450) system in 1981. The North American (AMPS 800) MHz system began service in 1983. (The definition of some of the many national and international cellular systems are given in Appendix 1 at the end of the text.)

When a mathematical model is applied to the cellular radio cell layout principle a honeycomb of hexagonal cells appears. This is the reason why a hexagonal pattern is generally associated with cellular radio on the covers of conference proceedings, books, etc.; however, in practice the real physical radio layout is less well defined.

1.4 Radio coverage by a single cell

A single radio cell and the factors which dictate coverage are illustrated in Figure 1.6. The base station will usually be well sited, have a suitable transmit power, say in excess of 10 W, a sensitive receiver, low noise figure, useful antenna gain and also be clear of site noise.

The mobile will have a limited transmitter power, especially in the portable mode, and an elementary antenna. A more sophisticated antenna at the base receiver to some extent is able to make up this loss of received power in the reverse path, but it is the reverse path which generally limits the radio range.

Three ranges are shown in the diagram.

(i) The operating range – distance: d

(ii) The maximum radio range, i.e. cell size limited by noise, propagation factors and transmitter power – called: R_{max}

(iii) The cell size designed for the system, which will be less than R_{max}, decided by the coverage and cell pattern considerations – called: R

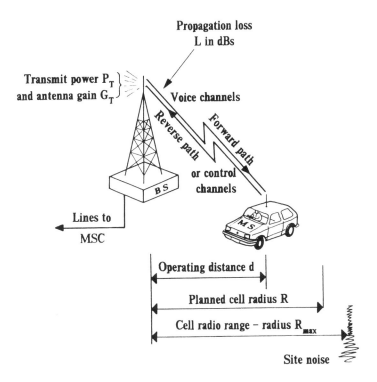

Figure 1.6 The fundamental radio cell and associated parameters

For a flat terrain, R can be regarded as the radius of the cell mapping a circle. The area covered will thus be πR^2 (km^2). Examples of coverage are shown in Table 1.1.

Table 1.1 Cell area and number of subscribers covered

Cell radius km^2	Coverage area km^2	Number of subscribers covered*
1	3.14	100
3	28.3	900
10	314	10,000
25	1960	60,000

* Assumes around 30 subscribers per sq. km as an initial assumption in order to get orders of magnitude. Note, a radius of 25 km relates to many of the major cities in the world, which tend to have populations in millions.

Adding a column showing the number of users which could be served by such a single cell illustrates how the single cell philosophy of producing radio-telephone coverage will break down or saturate.

The only way forward is to provide lots of small cells – the cellular principle.

Chapter 2 covers the physical principles on which cell radio coverage is established in practice and provides some numerical data for various conditions.

It turns out that for a large cell size, a high, well-mounted base station operating at VHF frequencies is best, but this is not at all practical for cities, etc. More realistically high UHF frequencies and base stations at building height provide compact cells in a city, where the large density of users are to be found, and many cells will be required. At the end of the day, however, the frequencies available are fixed by international agreement, which are discussed in due course.

Table 1.2 Classes and transmitter power of mobiles

Equipment type	Mobile Tx power	Antenna arrangement
IV Handportable*	< 1W	on set and shortened
II Transportable*	< 5W	on set
Vehicle mounted	> 10W	mounted on vehicle

* These can sometimes be plugged into a vehicle-mounted system.

The mobile depicted in Figure 1.6 shows a vehicle to emphasize mobility of the end user or subscriber. In practice three main types of mobile station can be defined as shown in Table 1.2, of which the so-called handportable makes up the bulk of the 100 M, or thereabouts, phones in use in the world today.

Clearly the radio coverage or cell size planning will need to take note of the type of user service anticipated, since a vehicle system may well have a 20 dB (or up to twice distance) advantage over a handportable, because of more favourable transmitter power and antenna positioning.

1.5 Multiple cell layout

Operation in a single cell is the domain of the well established and understood *private mobile radio* (PMR). The use of a *repeater* (central transmitter) can be likened to a central, well-placed base station and large areas can be covered by a single cell or repeater, i.e. 25 km radius or more at VHF. For greater coverage on-frequency (FM) or off-set frequency (AM) technology is or has been used. This is especially important for say police operations in rural areas. For the huge public domain services, or much lower power public radiotelephone concept of service, cell sizes will be very much smaller, but the same cell frequencies can in general not be used again in the adjacent areas.

Figure 1.5 illustrated this and the matter was also discussed, but three further factors now need attention:

- Can one have other frequencies in the adjacent cells?
- How does one manage the region of overlap?
- When can the same frequencies be used again?

The first point emphasizes that a cellular radio system will need a *block allocation* of frequencies. Whether the voice and signalling (control) are managed on a time division, a frequency division, or some hybrid arrangement does not matter, what is important is that much more bandwidth than the bandwidth required by the subscribers in the area of a single cell must be allocated.

This point also emphasizes that a mechanism must exist for handing over, called *handover,* the subscriber's radio connection from the frequencies used in one cell, say G, to the frequencies used in the next cell C, as he or she roams the service area of the cells.

This is the feature essential to any cellular radio operation, whether one is considering very small cell sizes (*micro-cells*), or average, or large cells – sometimes called *macro-cells*. Much of the complexity within a cellular radio unit, depicted in Figure 1.3, the frequency synthesizer, control and memory functions, are there mainly to handle handover. The radiotelephone circuit system must also be frequency agile to operate in a cellular system. However, other benefits also arise from this attribute, as described later.

The second point is the question of the physical overlap of cell coverage – not a feature apparent in drawings of cellular radio and many other artistic renderings of architectural and artifact aspects with a cellular appearance. The mobile will not know that it is in such a region unless it undertakes a scan of the spectrum. Often only the base station will know and clearly base stations must be able to communicate with each other. There is therefore a need for an overlay network of communication associated with each BS in Figure 1.5. This network, which can be regarded as a fixed network, can be realized by cable, microwave link or even satellite link.

With the existence of such a connection, station G can communicate to station C say, and they can decide between themselves when to take command of the subscriber moving through the region of overlap; the process of handover. The practical strategy used will depend on the system and other factors and is a fairly complex signal control mechanism.

The fact that several channels or frequencies are used in just one cell in order to accommodate many subscribers, plus the fact that further sets of frequencies must be used in adjacent cells, brings us to the third point; namely, when can the same frequencies be used again? This is the fundamental feature of cell layout and the usual strategy using hexagonal cells and is described in Chapter 3. The matter is also discussed further in Chapter 7.

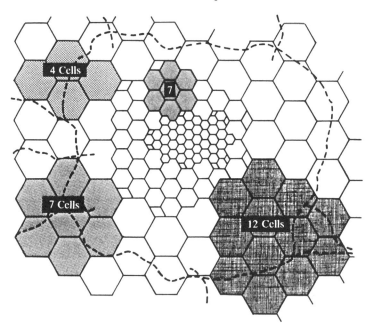

Figure 1.7 A typical city cellular radio cell plan; the cells are smaller where the most users are expected. Cluster sizes of 4, 7 and 12 cells are also indicated

As an example of a cell layout plan, Figure 1.7 shows the plan for London, UK, at an early stage of implementation. The layout plan illustrates three features useful to the present discussion.

• Cell sizes are made smaller at the centre of a city or area of occupation of most subscribers.

- Cells are arranged in *clusters*. Only certain cluster sizes are possible, principally due to the geometry of a hexagon, and the allowable cluster sizes of 4, 7 and 12 are shown by way of illustration.

- Cell splitting is a permissible operation, that is, installing additional base stations, within, or at the *corners* of a cell, when an increased density of coverage is warranted.

1.6 The fixed supporting network

The fixed supporting network associated with a cellular radio scheme, an outline of which is sketched in Figure 1.8, which is a sophisticated network, has several fundamental tasks:

- To connect all the base stations (BS) to each other for the purpose of communicating signals and messages to and from subscribers operating in the network. The modern trend is to use *base station controllers* (BSC) controlling a BS cluster. (In analog cellular the controller forms part of the mobile switching centres, for example, see Figure 3.20.)

- To provide switching centres so that traffic can be directed around the network. The centres are called *mobile switching centres* (MSC). An MSC does not have to be associated with every cluster of cells, such as the seven shown in Figure 1.5, but they are usually sited at convenient town centres for example.

As a cellular radio network grows, and the number of subscribers increases, the mobile switching centres have to begin handling a very large amount of traffic. What could have begun as a fairly small switch, e.g. 1000×1000 crosspoints, that is 1000 lines connecting another 1000 lines, must expand to a full capacity fixed telephone exchange.

- Again, as with the normal public switched telephone network (PSTN), full intermeshing of MSCs becomes very costly and therefore a second tier of overlay *transit switching centres* (TSC) is now common in cellular networks, giving a hierarchical network as associated with the fixed telephone network.

- Often a TSC will be delegated as a *gateway mobile switching centre* (GMSC). This has the special function of routing services within a cellular service into a fixed telephone network, i.e. the PSTN, or vice versa.

- With each mobile switching centre will be associated registers, rather like electronic telephone directories, known as a *home location register* (HLR) and a *visitors located register* (VLR). The registers themselves need not be physically associated with the location of their MSC, since the fixed network gives full connectivity, but they are part and parcel of the routing operation and are inevitable close to one or another MSC.

- Also, *authentication* is provided for a subscriber attempting to use the network. Authentication is usually associated with the home location registers, but is shown as a separate centre (AUC). All equipment used on the network, whether a handportable, or vehicle-mounted phone carries an electronic identity number, or equipment identity number. This used to be a number programmed into the mobile on registration by a service provider, but has now expanded to fifteen digits called the *international mobile equipment identity* (IMEI), consisting of

  - A type approval code
  - A factory (assembly part) code
  - A serial number unique to MS type

An *equipment identity register* (EIR) checks out the status of the subscriber identity number. These centres are all shown in Figure 1.8.

- The time of use of the network by a subscriber is also recorded in a *billing centre*. In general the charge made is independent of the physical distance separating two users of the same network, since even if the callers are in adjacent cells, or in the same cell, the full cellular fixed network is really put into use. Clearly, some regional strategy can be put into operation, but this consideration has no bearing on the principles of cellular radio.

- Finally, the fixed network, outlined in Figure 1.8, will have (if agreed) a trunk connection into the existing fixed network. This gives the connectivity between the fixed subscribers and mobile subscribers. The fixed subscriber will use a mobile identification number to call; the mobile subscriber will use the usual area code number. In both cases billing will be made at the mobile tariff rate.

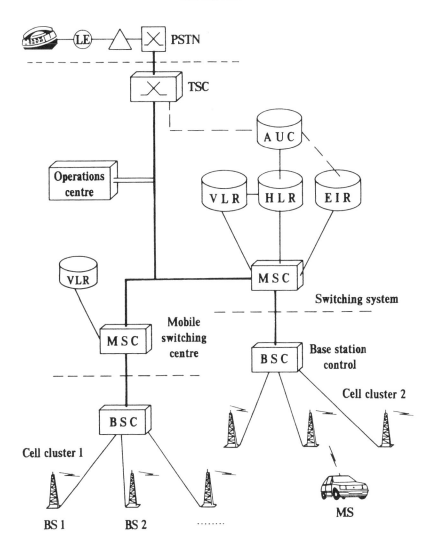

Figure 1.8 A fixed network supporting a cellular radio system showing the various major components

In practice several more mobile switching centres and base stations will exist, but all the main components referred to above are shown. In addition a *network management centre* (NMC), which can include the *operations and maintenance centre* (OMC), is indicated. There will basically be one such centre for each network in general. Its role, as the name implies, includes the following network management functions:

Fault diversion strategies can be implemented

Extra traffic routing is supervised

Interference conditions are recorded

Maintenance programs are run

Subscriber base and income are monitored

1.7 Radio frequencies available

We have so far been able to discuss cellular radio without referring to a specific frequency or specific band of frequencies. Not many years ago cellular radio was synonymous with the frequencies 800-900 MHz. Any reference to these UHF frequencies seemed to imply cellular radio. Nowadays, it is recognized that cellular does not have to be associated with a specific band of frequencies; in fact cellular networks exist which range from VHF to microwave frequencies.

There are constraints, however, on those frequencies that can be assigned; these are:

- The international agreements to use certain bands of frequency for certain uses, e.g. broadcasting, mobile radio, navigation, etc. Such decisions are made at World Administrative Radio Conferences (WARC), now held at fairly frequent intervals (in years). In practice, for the allocation of frequencies the world has been divided into three regions. These are shown in Figure 1.9. Often, for historic or geographical reasons, the allocation of frequencies in the three regions has varied.

This could well mean that a cellular service in one region could not be applied directly in another region as the allocation for frequencies is outside the plans of the other region. Some cross border conflict between countries edging regions 1 and 3 could arise for example, but if one takes the Gobi desert straddling these regions as an example, the problem perhaps is not too critical!

- More serious are the National Frequency Allocations. These are the allocation of frequencies by the government or body vested with the right to allocate frequencies on a country by country basis. The frequencies so allocated are listed in the national radio frequency allocation tables, that is, a book listing such frequencies and their uses. These generally differ considerably.

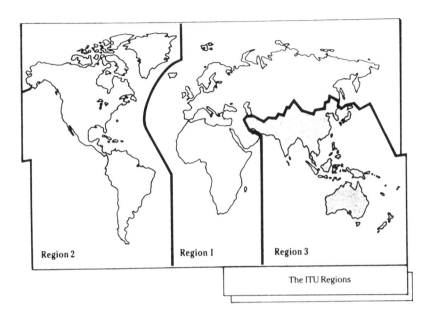

Figure 1.9 The three regions in the world according to the International Tele-communications Union (ITU)

What we shall find is that several cellular radiotelephone systems are in existence (as set out in Appendix 1), not from principle, but from frequency allocation. These differences exist especially in so-called *analog cellular,* where digital signalling using frequency shift keying modulation is coupled with analog voice using frequency modulation, and which operate on a *frequency division multiple access* (FDMA) strategy.

On the other hand, the attraction of using fully *digital cellular,* where both the signalling and encoded speech are digital and more closely attuned to the digital operated fixed network structure, has necessitated such massive research and development, that single regional cellular networks are being accepted in regionally agreed frequency bands. Most of these latest systems are planned on a *time division multiple access* (TDMA) format, but a complete switch to TDMA is not practical, due to the vagaries of radio propagation in cells at high radio frequencies. A breakdown of the frequencies used is initally given in Chapter 3, with details of the lower microwave bands in Chapter 9, p. 234.

1.8 The radio carrier and some attributes

Because the radio carrier is so fundamental to cellular radio some general comments are useful at this point. The loss of power on propagation and operation of antennas are considered in the next chapter, while the problem of the signal reaching both base and mobile by several paths – called multipath propagation – is described in Chapter 5.

For the moment we have in Figure 1.10(a), a carrier wave of a signal frequency f_c. It reaches a peak of amplitude twice every cycle, and also crosses zero at twice the cycle rate $t_c = 1/f_c$. An important projection is as a *phasor*, Figure 1.10(b). The amplitude of a phasor has a constant (peak) amplitude. Its direction defines the carrier phase with respect to a particular time datum. This phasor is projected further to show a progressive (radio) wave, depicted Figure 1.10(c). This latter diagram will be recalled in the next chapter. Also shown is a second possible carrier wave of the same frequency, but in phase quadrature. This wave travels forward with the first wave, but always remains 90° out of phase in the space plane.

The projection here is imaginary, however, because it really represents two components which are each a carrier wave, but now drawn as one on paper rotated through 90°. If we were to project the second carrier back to (a) we would obtain a single carrier wave, but whose sent amplitude was $\sqrt{2}$ times larger.

If on the other hand the two carrier waves were of a slightly different frequency, that is $f_1 - f_2 = \Delta f$, the phasor of f_2 would be rotating at a slightly different speed compared to f_1, and therefore would appear to have a progressively changing phase (and zero crossing times). The appearance of projection (c) could be kept very similar, but the appearance of projection (a) would be that of two waves beating. The beat frequency is the difference frequency Δf. This concept is important to us when multipath propagation is discussed, since it is then easier to understand signal fading and other related properties.

The concept is also very important to us when we consider modulation, in Chapter 6. In analog cellular, *frequency modulation* (FM) is used. Clearly, what one does here is to rotate the phase back and forth in sympathy with the voice waveform signal, because the instantaneous frequency is changed. The mobile, or base, receiver demodulator has therefore to follow the phasor around the phase circle faithfully.

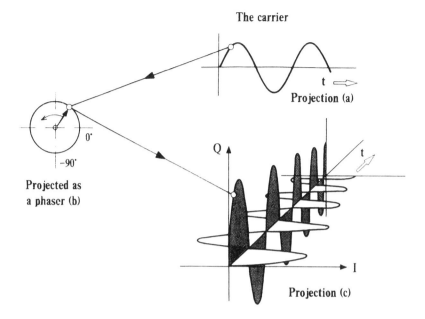

Figure 1.10 A carrier wave depicted as (a) a conventional waveform, (b) projected as a phasor, and (c) projected into phase space and two carriers progressing

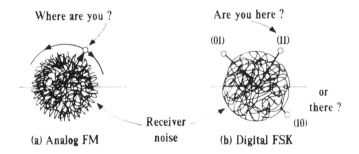

Figure 1.11 A frequency modulated carrier vector subject to noise, (a) analog FM case (b) digital FSK case

This works well until the noise level in the system (site plus receiver circuits) becomes excessive, as suggested in Figure 1.11(a); just beyond this threshold, the noise phasors take over and the receiver output (radiotelephone arrangement) becomes noisy and unusable. This limit is set by the carrier-to-noise ratio (C/N), usually measured as a power ratio in dB, at the receiver. The effect is demonstrated in Figure 1.12. As is well known the output of the radio becomes 'all' noise, known as *FM capture*.

The result is also referred to again in Figure 6.4; an acceptable speech-to-noise performance collapses on reaching a threshold of about 13 dB. This defines the distance R_{max} in a cell site. Clearly, it would be undesirable to approach this FM threshold point too closely; therefore handover is arranged by observing, at the base site, when a C/N ratio of say +20 dB is reached. This defines the cell radius R. Note that one has therefore implied that the C/N ratio is used to effect handover in analog cellular.

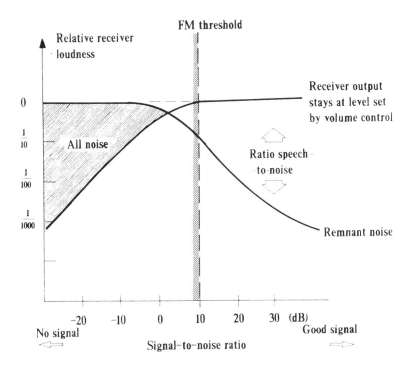

Figure 1.12   The capture effect in FM demodulation indicating acceptable signal-to-noise ratios at a receiver

The situation is different in digital cellular. The modulation will be a digital modulation which can in general be regarded as being a *frequency shift keying* (FSK) format, where at any specific digit symbol time-of-occurrence, the carrier will find itself in some specific phase location space, as depicted in Figure 1.11(b). Noise or interference in this case is shown as confusing the wanted signal phasor. The receiver demodulator does not now produce additional noise, but the decoded data now contains incorrectly recovered data, giving rise to what are called bit errors. These are measured as the bit error rate or ratio

(BER); for example with one error in 100 bits, BER $= 1 \times 10^{-2}$, in 1000 bits, the BER $= 1 \times 10^{-3}$, etc. In fixed computer networks one assumes really no errors, or perhaps a BER of less than 1×10^{-11}.

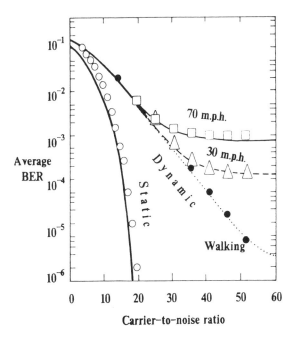

Figure 1.13   The dependence of bit error rate (BER) on carrier-to-noise ratio and the operating conditions of the mobile receiver

In contrast, in mobile radio such a low error rate is extremely unlikely. A more likely performance is suggested in Figure 1.13. This diagram brings out several points which we need note.

• The static case refers to the particular digital signalling technology chosen, as discussed in Chapter 6.

• The dynamic case refers to the mobile situation. The faster the subscriber travels the more serious the BER problem becomes. This is due to a relationship between the multipath signal characteristics and the travelling speed of the mobile.

• In certain situations the BER can reach an *irreducible level*. Increased radio power within the cell is of no avail. Emphasis must therefore be put on *forward error correcting* (FEC) strategies. FEC thus becomes a major aspect of signalling within a cellular radio system.

A major distinction now arises between digital and analog cellular. Whereas analog (for voice) degrades slowly, as the subscriber walks into a building or drives into an area of weak signal for example, because the digital systems uses coded speech (Chapter 7), the speech recovery mechanism will collapse at some specific BER threshold, say 5×10^{-2}. The effect is illustrated in Figure 1.14. This shows the voice quality factor (called mean opimon score in Chapter 7) conceptually plotted against the received C/N ratio. The analog system degrades gracefully, as they say, but a digital system can collapse (no service) quite suddenly. This necessitates the use of a more detailed coverage strategy for digital cellular, which we shall come to in due course.

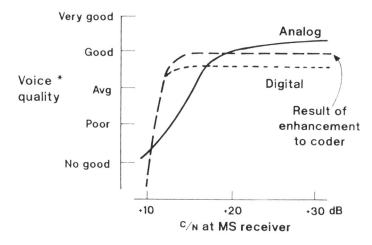

Figure 1.14   The collapse of speech quality as the carrier-to-noise ratio at a MS receiver worsens. The same is true on the reverse path, but the mobile subscriber is not as aware of this happening. (*Background noise level is not fully included on this scale.)

1.9 Control and channel signalling

A mobile radiotelephone system differs from a fixed telephone network in the important operational aspect of *roaming*, or rather the subscriber being able to appear anywhere within the network at anytime. Whereas many years ago all telephones tended to be black and have a sameness, mobility brought with it a need for a more colourful system and active system management. To some extent we have an analogy with the historic system of signalling in the Navy; a ship would show its colours in order to be identified, or to pass messages. So in cellular radio coloured messages are exchanged between subscribers and their mobile phone sailing through the system.

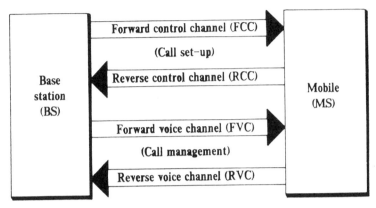

(This scheme principally applies to AMPS and TACS)

Figure 1.15   The control and signalling channels associated with an analog cellular system

More specifically there are four channels set up between a mobile and its associated base as shown in Figure 1.15 and implied in Figure 1.6. In FDMA systems, such as TACS and AMPS these would be four radio channels, two at a time. In digital TDMA systems such as GSM and PCS the channels would be allocated time slots; pairs allocated to control, other pairs allocated to the phone conversation and its management. Other variations are possible, such as in the Nordic Mobile telephone (NMT) system where channels have reversible roles.

In general control channels (or time slots) are used to page or call the mobile and also acts as 'beacons' for a mobile entering an operational area. A response from the mobile is required by the system in order to check its identity, (friend or foe) and whether it is within satisfactory communications range. Thus cellular radio depends very much on a handshaking procedure. In addition the cells are colour coded by a simple two-bit symbol, called the *digital colour code* (DCC), assigned to the control channels; this assists the system to manage frequency (or time slot) assignment in a cluster of cells. Hence the analogy with naval operations. When agreement has been reached between the mobile and the system, which takes place by means of a medium speed digital signal using a *high-level data link control* (HDLC) format, the system and mobile set up the communication circuit on the *voice* channels, as indicated in Figure 1.15. Here again *supervisory audio tone* (SAT) signals are an important part of the final handshaking or call set-up operation. Cell clusters are now SAT coloured by three tones. An illustration of the whereabouts of the DCC coding and SAT allocations in a cellular radio cell coverage group is given in Figure 1.16.

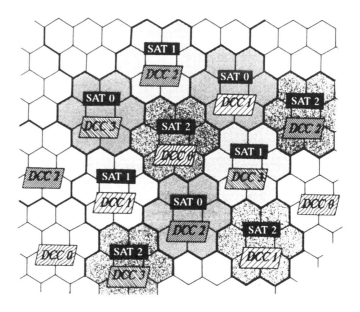

Figure 1.16   Cell layout plan showing allocation of DCC codes and SAT tones in analog
cellular

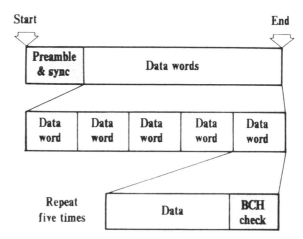

Figure 1.17   Signalling message format on the control channel. In the TACS system, for
example, these are the beacon frequencies specific to each operator

For the majority of control interchanges analog cellular uses high speed digital signalling with high redundancy to give high reliability even in poor radio conditions. Each signalling word is repeated several times, and at the receive end a bit-by-bit majority decision is performed which corrects the burst and random errors. The signalling word is further protected by a BCH block code (see below), which is used to check for residual errors, and allows for up to one remaining bit error to be corrected. A typical frame is shown in Figure 1.17.

On the base-to-mobile signalling link or voice channels, where it is particularly important that handover commands are correctly received, often under poor and rapidly degrading radio conditions, signalling messages carry an even higher redundancy, and are repeated up to eleven times, as indicated in Figure 1.18.

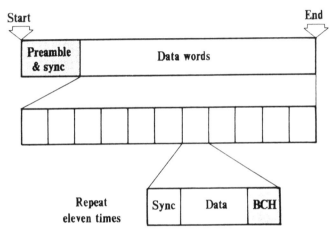

Figure 1.18 Signalling message format on voice channels

Depending on the network, the network uses a set of control channels which carry only signalling. The channel numbers of the control channels are pre-designated, and all mobile stations operating in the network have these numbers permanently programmed in their memory.

Functionally, there are three types of control channel:

Dedicated control channels

Paging channels

Access channels

Physically, however, all three functions may be combined on each of the control channels, and in practice this is normally the case. Most standards allow for the separation of paging and access functions into separate physical channels, and for the extension of the total number of control channels in cases where the amount of signalling activity is greater than can be handled by the combined control channels.

The functions carried by the various control channels may be summarized as follows:

- Dedicated control channels – unidirectional (base-to-mobile) – used to carry basic system parameters and information on the channel numbers of the paging channels currently in use.

- Paging channels – unidirectional (base-to-mobile) – used to carry basic system parameters, location area identity, and paging messages to specific mobiles for incoming call set-up.

- Access channels – bidirectional – in the mobile-to-base direction, used to pass information to the base station concerning the call set-up request or location registration by the mobile; in the base-to-mobile direction, they are used to confirm location registrations and to assign a voice channel following a call set-up request.

The signalling within the fixed network of a cellular system is identical to that used within all present-day digital fixed telephone networks and runs according to CCITT (telephone and telegraph committee of the ITU) standards. Because digital cellular technology is much more closed tuned to the modern digital fixed telephone technology, a fuller description of the fixed network in support of mobile phones is deferred until Chapter 9.

1.10 Error correction strategies

It is widely recognized that in practice mobile radio signals in any radio band, but more specifically at VHF and UHF, are always subject to variable received amplitude, changing phase and indeed spectrum widening due to a propagation induced frequency modulation. This is the phenomenon of *multipath reception*; the signal components from one base transmitter appear to come by different paths and directions to the mobile and give rise to these multipath effects.

Cellular radio can be designed in principle without giving much regard to multipath propagation. Narrowband analog FM voice transmission performs acceptably well, provided that careful voice bandwidth shaping is introduced in the transmitting and receiving *baseband* circuits. The problem comes with the control signals used to set up and manage the system, i.e. the signalling procedures just described above. Multipath now causes real difficulty due to error generation and false signalling. The specifics of multipath are described in more detail in Chapter 5 and in particular the concept of *coherence bandwidth* and its inverse, the *delay spread* are introduced. When the bit rate used for signalling becomes comparable with the delay spread (measured in microseconds), error correction strategies become vital.

There are three approaches to error correction. One is the *automatic repeat request* (ARQ) arrangement outlined in Figure 1.19. This method is used in a data specific cellular system described later in Chapter 4. It is not practical for a voice services since a lot of delay can be generated, i.e. the speech received would not necessarily be continuous.

On the other hand *forward error correction* (FEC) aims to correct the message once and for all. Like ARQ, forward error correction has to be implemented at both the mobile and the base, and vice versa, so there is a penalty on hardware and power consumption in the mobile, especially if it is handportable. FEC implementation is indicated in Figure 1.20.

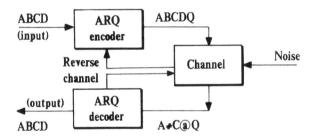

Figure 1.19 Automatic repeat request system

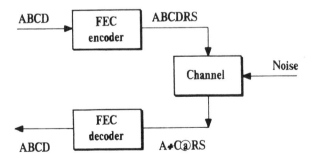

Figure 1.20 Forward error correction implementation in a system

In order to discuss the FEC options we need to define the type of signal message likely to be encountered. The smallest unit of data is the *bit;* a *symbol* may be formed by several bits if a multi-level modulation scheme is used. A group of symbols are then made up into a frame. Figure 1.21 shows a frame made up of 9 symbols with three bits per symbol; however, only some are *message* symbols, several could be redundant symbols introduced for the purpose of forward error correction.

In TDMA systems, as described in Chapter 8 and beyond, a single frame as shown here is now deemed a *time slot* (TS) within a full frame made up of several time slots – all carrying different data.

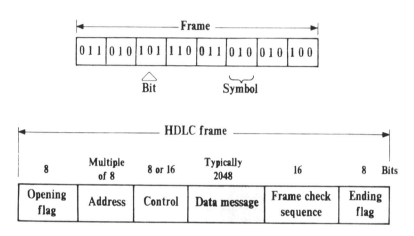

Figure 1.21 The construction of an HDLC frame and nature of bits and symbols

The encoder takes a set of k *message* symbols, which must be transmitted (pure data), appends to them r *check* symbols, and transmits the entire block of $n = k + r$ *channel* symbols per codeword. The result is denoted an (n,k) code. If the channel noise distorts sufficiently few of these n transmitted symbols, the r check symbols will provide the receiver with sufficient information to enable it to detect and correct the channel errors. Since each codeword contains n symbols and conveys k symbols of information, the theoretical information rate is reduced by the ratio k/n.

There are two major classes of error-correcting codes, *block codes* and *convolutional codes,* and the essential difference between them is as follows. In a block code, the n-symbol codeword generated by the encoder in a particular time unit depends only on the k message-symbols received within that time unit. In a convolutional code, the frame of n code-symbols generated in that time unit depends not only on the current message frame, but also on the preceding $N - 1$ message frames, where N is referred to as the constraint length. Hence, as each incoming information bit propagates through the encoder, it influences several outgoing bits, thereby spreading the information content of each message bit among several adjacent code bits. Usually the values of k and n are small; in fact, many convolutional techniques operate with a code efficiency of 50%, i.e. one check bit inserted after each information bit.

Under convolutional codes, the Viterbi code corrects random error-patterns, that is, patterns in which any one particular bit has as much chance of being distorted as do the bits immediately preceding or following it. Such an error distribution arises from *additive white Gaussian noise* (AWGN). Block codes, on the other hand, correct burst errors, i.e. where a number of errors occur closely together, separated by a large guard-space (or error-free zone). Such an error distribution arises from impulse noise and there is a dependence of error probabilities in successively transmitted bits.

Under block codes, the Reed-Solomon and Golay codes have both burst and random error-correcting abilities; the former treats non-binary data, whereas the latter handles only binary data. The Reed-Solomon code is a special sub-class of the Bose-Chaudhuri-Hocquenghem (BCH) code, with powerful applications for correcting multiple bursts of errors in a frame. BCH codes themselves are a sub-class of the cyclic codes, which in turn belong to the family of linear block-codes. The Golay code is capable of correcting a combination of 3 or fewer errors in a block of 23 bits and is the only known multiple-error-correcting binary perfect code.

A simplified family tree of codes is given in Figure 1.22, showing the relative positions of the codes within the coding hierarchy.

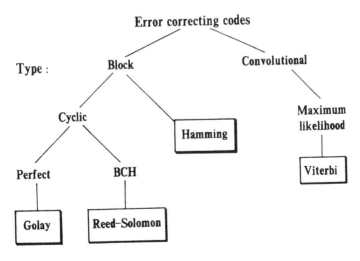

Figure 1.22 An error-correcting code hierarchy diagram

One might well question how efficient these error-correcting codes are. The information rate has to be reduced, which in turn implies fewer bits per bandwidth of the radio channel allocation.

Much study of this matter has taken place, to some extent prompted by deep space satellite experiments, where the received signal is at the edge of detectability. This limit was defined by Shannon, who showed that the theoretical limit of the detectability of an energy per bit E_b, to Gaussian average noise power per unit bandwidth N_0, can be -1.6 dB. Practical systems need many decibels of power above this level. Figure 1.13 showed how BER changes versus received carrier-to-noise power ratio for a typical mobile radio system. Translated into the BER versus the ratio E_b/N_0 (described further in Chapter 6), shows that any particular modulation, such as *differential phase shift keying* (DPSK), needs many decibels of excess received power as compared to the Shannon limit, i.e. Figure 1.23.

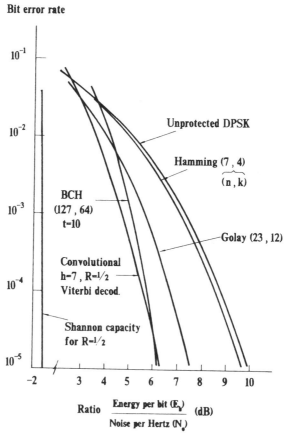

Figure 1.23   Improvement of BER performance by specific error-correcting codes and the Shannon limit

However, adding the FEC codes described above, shows how much improvement can be gained, especially if initially the error rate was less than one bit wrong in, say, 200 bits. The error rate can be improved to 1 in 10,000. However, only when the pure data channel is relatively free of errors, can any significant reduction in the ratio E_b /N_o be made. In all cases, however, FEC introduces the penalty of a slower throughput of data.

Finally, a strategy called *interleaving* may be used. Because the signal over a mobile radio path can very often *fade* briefly, some data could be entirely lost. ARQ is not practical, but if a strategy of 'reshuffling' the data stream temporarily is employed – called interleaving – it is then possible to recover critical parts, especially with regard to the speech coding algorithm, by this means. A signal delay penalty is implied, as can be appreciated from Figure 1.24. The application of interleaving to the GSM digital cellular method is described in Chapter 9.

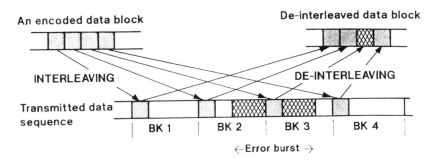

Figure 1.24 Interleaving and de-interleaving for a specific data block

1.11 Numbering plans

Although we have referred to numbering plans earlier in this introductory chapter, the number plans associated with the fixed network (PSTN) and more especially the mobile equipment identification is quite complicated and expansion of some points is worthwhile at this stage.

The original numbering plan for the international telephone network is described in CCITT (the International Telegraph and Telephone Consultative Committee) Recommendation E.163. In this scheme each country or zone is assigned a country code of 1, 2 or 3 digits, with a maximum international number length of 12 digits (excluding access prefixes such as 0, 00 and 010, etc.). This scheme served until the early 1980s when consideration was given to the numbering aspects of the *integrated services digital network* (ISDN). The

Cellular Radio

numbering plan for the ISDN needs to evolve from the PSTN, so the numbering plan for ISDN is an evolution of the existing E.163 Recommendation.

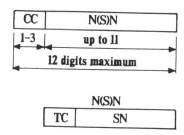

CC   : Country code
N(S)N : National (significant) number
TC   : Trunk code
SN   : Subscriber number

Figure 1.25 E.163 number structure

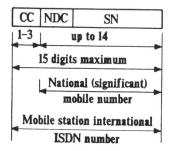

CC   : Country code
NDC : Network destination code
SN   : Subscriber number

Figure 1.26 The E.164 number structure and mobile numbering structure

This is known as Recommendation E.164 'The numbering plan for the ISDN era' and was approved in 1984. The main principles of E.163 remain, but with the introduction of an increased international number length to 15 digits, and the introduction of a *network destination code* (NDC) in place of the E.163 trunk code. E.163 only allows for up to 2 digits to determine the international route; this gave a variable maximum number analysis of 3 to 5 digits, depending on the length of the country code; in E.164 this was fixed at a maximum of 6 digits including country code, as indicated in Figure 1.26. This change reflects the increased capability of *stored program control* (SPC) exchanges.

The arrangements for the implementation of the E.164 plan specifies the date of 31 December 1996 for bringing the recommendation into effect. The present world fixed network numbering zones, as set out in Table 1.3, are to be maintained, however.

Table 1.3 World fixed network numbering zones

Code	Zone
1	North America (including Hawaii and the Caribbean)
2	Africa
3 and 4	Europe
5	South America and Cuba
6	South Pacific (Australasia)
7	USSR
8	North Pacific (Eastern Asia)
9	Far East and Middle East

The identification plan for telephone subscribers (fixed or mobile) is contained in CCITT Recommendation E.212, and the allocation of mobile station roaming numbers is defined in E.164. The number consists of:

- *Country code* (CC) of the country in which the mobile station is registered, followed by,

- National (significant) mobile number which consists of *network destination code* (NDC) and *subscriber number* (SN).

The number of digits used for identification is limited to a twelve-digit code, made up of the CC, the NDC and the SN.

For mobile services, one notes the term *mobile station international ISDN number* (MSISDN). For mobile users, especially on the GSM network, where international roaming is a key feature, the number is better known as a *mobile station roaming number* (MSRN). This has the same structure as that shown in Figure 1.26, except that the country code is now the *mobile country code* (MCC), which one notes is different from the CC used by the fixed PSTN, the network destination code also now refers to activity in the *public land mobile network* (PLMN), and finally the *subscriber number* (SN), which is usually a six digit subscriber number. Table 1.4 shows some MCC numbers and their respective PLNM network numbers currently agreed by roaming agreements.

Table 1.4 Examples of mobile station roaming number codes

Zone	Country	Country Code	Network Code*
2	Belgium	206	01
2	Italy	222	01, 02
2	Malta	278	–
3	Canada	302	–
3	Barbados	342	–
3	Bahamas	364	–
4	Jordan	416	#
4	Qatar	427	#
4	UAE	424	01
5	Australia	505	02, 03
5	Fiji	542	–
5	Singapore	525	01
6	Egypt	602	–
6	Morocco	604	01
6	South Africa	655	01, 10

* Two codes means two operators available; a blank means no operator (at the time of writing); a # means connection awaited.

1.12 Summary of important features

Although many cellular systems exist and are being implemented in the world today, it can be said that they all depend on certain basic principles, despite previously being totally incompatible in many ways. Thus, we can define the following list of features that the systems have *in common,* namely:

- At any instant, all subscribers (the mobile) operate in a single numbered radio cell. This is now given the name *cell global identity* (CGI).

- The radio properties of a cell are those of propagation coverage and multipath effects.

- The cell is one of a very large number laid out on a specific plan arrangement, made up of clusters of cells.

- The frequencies assigned to each cell in a cluster are repeatedly used in other clusters.

- The mobile therefore operates expecting both co-channel and adjacent channel interference.

- The mobile must register with a fixed telecommunications network which controls the operation of all the cells. This is called the public land mobile network, as opposed to the public fixed telephone network. The fixed network can be interconnected to the public telephone network.

- The network can assist the mobile to be handed over from one cell to another as it moves geographically. This provides the roaming and a no-fixed-abode facility.

- To manage these last two features the mobile must be constantly signalling to and from the fixed network.

- The message channels are duplex and can be voice or data.

- The mobile telephone must be frequency agile and carry batteries and be given an identity number.

Differences between cellular radio systems come about because of the following features:

- The radio frequency band(s) allocated to the specific service.
- The mode-of-operation can be all-digital or analog plus digital.

- All-digital systems allow time division access as the method of enhancing the number of subscribers within one cell.

- Mixed systems use frequency division access methods for sorting out subscribers.

- There are variations of the basic parameters of the FDMA and TDMA systems.

- The above mode-of-operation differences give rise to different handover strategies and details of the fixed network architecture.

- The more recent systems have only been made possible by developments in VLSI circuit technology.

In all cases the density of radio cells within a geographical area, and the effective number of radio channels available, determine the capacity of a system, and this is discussed in the last chapter.

Further reading

A Guide to TACS – Total Access Communication Systems. (1985). DTI, UK

Boucher, N.J. (1990). *Cellular Radio Handbook,* Quantum Publishing Inc, USA

Clark, G.C. and Cain, J.B. (1981). *Error-correction Coding for Digital Communications,* Plenum Press, NY

Ericsson Review, (1987). 'Special issue on cellular radio telephony', No 64

Farrell, P.G. (1990). 'Coding as a cure for communication calamities', *Elec Comms Eng* J., December, pp 213-220

Lee, W.C.Y. (1989). *Mobile Cellular Communications Systems,* McGraw-Hill Book Co, NY

Young, W. R. (1979). 'Advance mobile phone service: Introduction, background and objective', *B.S.T.J.,* 58, pp 1-41

Some recent textbooks dealing with cellular radio

Balston, D M. and Macario R.C.V. (1993). *Cellular Radio Systems,* Artech House.

Gardiner, J. and West, B. (1995). *Personal Communications Systems and Technologies,* Artech House.

Gibson, D. (Ed) (1996). *The Mobile Communication Handbook,* CRC Press, in co-operation with IEEE.

Lee, C.Y. (1992). *Mobile Communications Design Fundamentals,* Second Edition, Wiley.

Macario, R.C.V. (Ed) (1996). *Modern Personal Radio Systems,* The IEE Press.

Mehrotra, A. (1994). *Cellular Radio Analog and Digital Systems*, Artech House.

Mehrotra, A. (1994). *Cellular Radio Performance Engineering*, Artech House.

Mouly, M. and Pautet, M. (1992). *The GSM System for Mobile Communications*. Published by the authors, Paris.

Rappaport, T.S. (1996). *Wireless Communications, Principles and Practice*, Prentice Hall and IEEE Press.

Steele, R. (1992). *Mobile Radio Communications*, Pentech Press.

Wong, P. and Britland, D. (1995) *Mobile Data Communication Systems*, Artech House.

2 Radio Coverage Prediction

2.1 Electromagnetic waves

Radio waves form part of the naturally occurring electromagnetic wave spectrum, any one frequency component of which can be represented as a progressive electromagnetic wave. Such a wave component is shown in Figure 2.1.

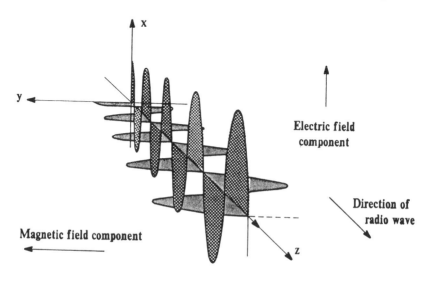

Figure 2.1 Representation of an electromagnetic (EM) wave moving through space showing the magnetic and electric oscillatory components

It is important to understand this diagram. Firstly, the wave travels forward in a specific direction and this is the basis of the concept of directivity of an antenna. The waveform repeats itself after a distance of one wavelength. For mobile radio this distance or wavelength ranges from metres to centimetres. Although the frequency of the wave, say 100 to 2000 MHz, is specified in the assignment of a channel to a mobile radio user, wavelength is more relevant to the radiation and reception of the EM wave when considering the antenna. Also the defects of propagation of the wave, such as destructive multipath, when replicas of the same wave arrive from different directions, takes more note of the wavelength.

Secondly, Figure 2.1 indicates that the EM wave has two active components, the electric field vector and the magnetic vector. These are in phase in time but not in space. The diagram shows a *vertically polarized* radio wave. This

38

polarization arose because of the way it was generated. Because there is a tendency to use vertically mounted dipoles or monopole antennas, vertical polarization ensues, with a vertical electrical field component, usually measured in microvolts per metre, or dBμV/m.

Also, unless one is able to markedly alter the electrical characteristics of free space, the magnetic component of the wave is closely related to the electric component value, from which one obtains the radiation power density (S) of the EM wave. This is measured as the electrical power (watts) passing through a one meter square, facing the direction of the wave.

The relation is given by the well known equation

$$S_R = \frac{E_R{}^2}{120\,\pi} \tag{2.1}$$

120π is called the intrinsic impedance of the free space, as can be seen from the relation between the voltage and power, and is approximately 377 ohms.

A third attribute of Figure 2.1 is that if the page of the book is rotated the effect of a change of polarization can be noted. Ninety degrees gives a horizontally polarized wave, which will not be so well detected by a vertically orientated electric antenna (dipole). It is to be noted that a change of polarization can occur at sharp angles of ground or building reflection. (It is perhaps worth pointing out that in the truly personal phone environment, the received signal will have its wave polarization altered due to reflections off the various building structures, etc., and for this reason handportable cellular phones continue to work, however held.)

A circularly polarized wave is one which has a continuous rotation of polarization induced into it by the radiating antenna structure. Current mobile radio systems use vertically polarized signals, but it may be found advantageous to use more complicated wave structures at new bands in excess of 1 GHz especially satellite; indeed the signal is most likely to be very complicated as shown in Chapter 5.

A final feature of Figure 2.1 is that the diagram only shows a single EM carrier wave, that is, a single frequency. An actual mobile radio signal will consist of a closely knit group of such waves, being a modulated carrier wave. The forward movement of the signal in a rigidly timed digital system has to be taken into account, but also certainly manifests itself under mobile conditions as described in Chapter 5 on multipath propagation, whatever technology is used.

2.2 Antenna considerations

In order to describe radio wave propagation it is necessary to have a basic appreciation of antenna theory, but the requirements can be kept very brief.

Thus the generation of the wave depicted in Figure 2.1 requires, for example, a conducting structure in which there is an oscillating electrical current.

The simplest antenna is known as a *dipole,* formed by separating the ends of a transmission line or coaxial cable. The structure is resonant, or rather matches to the transmission line, when the dipole has a total length of one half a wavelength, hence the name, *half wave dipole,* as indicated in Figure 2.2.

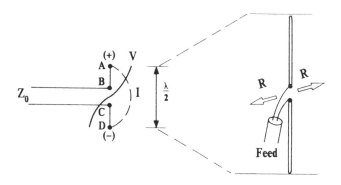

Figure 2.2 Open transmission line forming a half wave dipole

If the top section is mounted above a conducting surface, a monopole antenna is formed. This need only have one quarter of a wavelength in physical height. Thus at 900 MHz this implies a short metal rod of about 8.3 cm. Figure 2.3 shows the situation at the base of the antenna (the centre of the equivalent dipole).

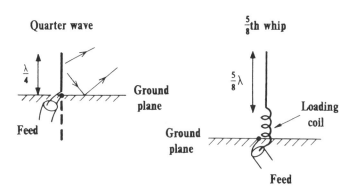

Figure 2.3 The roof mounted $\lambda/4$ monopole antenna. Extra effective height and gain can be obtained by a loading coil

The roof mounted monopole (half a dipole) is the best known example. The current oscillates in amplitude and absolute magnitude along the vertical structure and sends out radiation, mainly in the horizontal plane in which the antenna is situated. The fact that the radiation pattern is not isotropic implies directional gain (G). Gain and direction are related because antenna gain means a concentration of radiation in a particular direction. A short dipole has a gain of about 1.5 times (= 1.76 dB) compared to an isotropic or point source antenna.

Because simple dipole UHF antennas are physically small, they can be regarded as a point source when viewed at a distance from the base station or mobile.

For a mobile the antenna can be reduced in length (or size) by what is known as *coil loading*. Sometimes the base loading coil can be seen, i.e. as on a vehicle; alternatively a *helix* is encapsulated in a protected stub which acts as the antenna. Although the antenna remains resonant at the frequency band of operation its effectiveness as a receiving antenna is proportional to the physical height of the antenna. This fact needs to be observed when planning cell sizes.

At base stations the antenna can be more robust, as this gives system gain. Typically a stack of *folded dipoles* is used. Four are shown (vertically) in Figure 2.4. This arrangement will double the gain, i.e. add +3 dB, and double the bandwidth. The folded dipole responds more effectively over a wider band of frequencies.

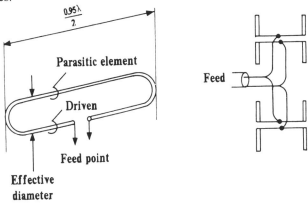

Figure 2.4 A folded dipole, also shown arranged as a stack of four

To obtain a *sectored* cell pattern a reflecting or director element would be associated with each active folded dipole. The directivity associated with the familiar TV Yagi antenna would be too great, say, less than a 30° beamwidth. Often a folded metal ridge reflector is used, with the fold corresponding to angle of the cell sector aimed at being illuminated. Three or six such antennas can be mounted around the top of a tower. The actual radiated signal can also be *tilted* down slightly.

When studying propagation and the associated antennas, it becomes helpful to think of an antenna as a collector of radiation, having a certain aperture. This aperture is called the *effective aperture* (A) of the antenna and is the planar size of the antenna, as far as a collector of radiation is concerned.

An antenna of aperture A collects a power P (watts), that is,

$$P = A.S_R \tag{2.2}$$

It can be shown that the gain G and aperture A of all antennas are related by the formula

$$G = \frac{4\pi}{\lambda^2} A \tag{2.3}$$

The formula is most easily understood by considering a microwave dish antenna. The aperture is approximately the dish area (allowing for some loss of efficiency); therefore as the size (diameter) increases, so does the gain.

For a short dipole,

$$A_{dipole} = G\frac{\lambda^2}{4\pi} = 1.5\frac{\lambda^2}{4\pi} = \frac{3\lambda^2}{8\pi} \tag{2.4}$$

This equation again emphasizes how small an aperture handportable equipment UHF antennas present to the radio signal in a radio cell.

Using the previous equations one can calculate the relation between the power received by a dipole (P_d) and the signal field strength (E) at the dipole. At 900 MHz the relationship is

$$P_d \text{ (dBm)} = -135 + E \text{ (dB}\mu\text{V/m)} \tag{2.5}$$

For example, with 10 μV/m, i.e. a 20 dB increase in E, $P_d = -115$ dBm, which is a typical receiver final sensitivity. Lowering the frequency of operation to, say 200 MHz, increases P_d to -103 dBm, as the aperture of a dipole tuned to 200 MHz is larger, because the wavelength is larger.

The signal power received is the critical factor in propagation, because it has to overcome the *noise power* N_R at the receiver input. With N_R in dBm, the received signal/noise ratio, expressed in decibels, will be

$$(S/N)_R = P_d - N_R \quad \text{(dB)} \tag{2.6}$$

The S/N ratio can be improved by having antenna gain. The result, with a receiving antenna of gain G_R, will be

$$(S/N)_R = P_d + G_R - N_R \quad \text{(dB)} \tag{2.7}$$

This is especially important at the BS, because the MS T_X power is weak, and needs to be made up by BS antenna gain.

2.3 Models for propagation

Models for radio propagation all begin with the concept of two point source antennas in free space separated by a *distance* d (km).

2.3.1 In free space

The radiation power density at the receiver of the signal from the *transmitter of source power* P_T will be

$$S_R = P_T/4\pi d^2 \quad \text{(watts/m}^2\text{)} \tag{2.8}$$

since the radiation is distributed over a sphere of radius d. If the transmitter antenna has a directivity gain G_T, in the direction of the receiver, the received signal increases to

$$S_R = G_T P_T/4\pi \, d^2 \tag{2.9}$$

Note that $G_T P_T$ is the *effective intrinsic radiated power* (EIRP) of the transmitter. Furthermore, if the receiving antenna has an aperture A, the power received, according to (2.2), is

$$P_R = S_R.A$$

therefore

$$P_R = S_R.G_R \, (\lambda^2/4\pi) \tag{2.10}$$

Introducing the value for S_R from (2.9) gives

$$P_R = (P_T/4\pi d^2).G_T.(\lambda^2/4\pi).G_R$$

or

$$P_R/P_T = G_T.G_R \ (\lambda/4\pi d)^2 \tag{2.11}$$

Note that directivity gain at either end of the system enhances the received signal, but there remains the fundamental free space propagation factor $(4\pi d/\lambda)^2$ which reduces the received power as compared to the transmitted power. This is called the *free space propagation loss factor* L, and is given by

$$L = (4\pi d/\lambda)^2 \tag{2.12}$$

L arises due to dispersion of the wave energy. L increases as the wavelength reduces, i.e. at higher frequencies. This equation is more often written in logarithmic form, using frequency (MHz) and distance (km),

$$L_{dB} = 32 + 20 \log f_{MHz} + 20 \log d_{km} \tag{2.13}$$

Example At 450 MHz over a path length of 1 km, the formula gives

$$L = 86 \text{ dB}$$

This loss, one should recall, applies in free space, or perhaps between two well sited microwave towers.

How does this relate to the transmitter power required to achieve effective communication? One needs knowledge of the receiver noise threshold N_R and the acceptable S/N ratio. Therefore P_T has to overcome N_R and L, but is helped by the antenna gains G_T and G_R.
  Therefore

$$P_T > (S/N) + N_R + L - G_T - G_R \ (dBm) \tag{2.14}$$

Typical observed noise levels are measured in dBm, but are shown in °K, using the fact that the *effective noise temperature* T_a creates the noise N_R, i.e.

$$N_R = k \, T_a \, B_w \tag{2.15}$$

where

    k   = Boltzmann's constant
        = 1.38 10^{-23} Watt sec/°K
    B_w = system bandwidth in Hertz

Therefore, at the reference temperature T_o one can calculate the fundamental noise level in a radio system, i.e.

using $T_a = T_o = 290$ °K $(+17°C)$,
$\therefore$ $N_o = -174$ dBm per Hz

Figure 2.5 shows how much the actual system noise level is above N_o; either as a *noise figure* F_a, or as a *noise temperature* T_a, relative to the reference noise temperature T_o. The data are then independent of the receiver bandwidth. Note that at UHF, receiver circuit noise and external site noise are comparable; together they limit the maximum cell size R_{max}.

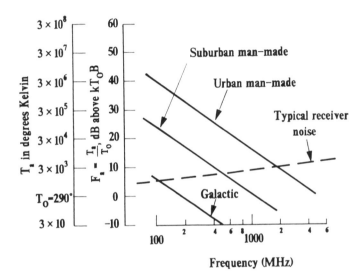

Figure 2.5 Typical noise levels for a UHF receiver

Example Same UHF signal over 1 km, and using

S/N   = +20 dB , say
N_R = −120 dBm
L   = 86 dB
G_T, G_R = −3 dB (handportables - helical antennas), say

Therefore, using Eqn (2.14), one finds

$P_T > -8.0$ dBm
  $= 160$ microwatts

which is a very low power.

This is the free space result. On the ground, specular reflection modifies the received signal, as shown in Figure 2.6.

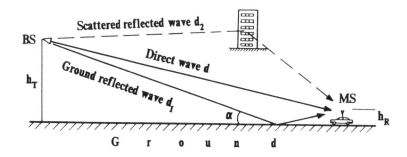

Figure 2.6 The direct wave, ground reflected wave and one scattered wave in the mobile radio environment

2.4 Reflections at a boundary

Two types of reflected wave are indicated: one reflected off the ground (terrain) and onto the mobile; the other reflected or scattered from a surrounding building or hillside. The reflection of an electromagnetic wave at a *boundary*,

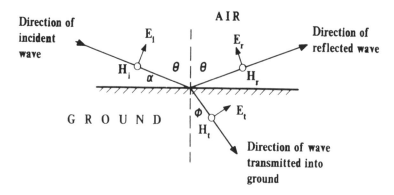

Figure 2.7 The EM wave components transmitted due to a boundary

that is a surface where there is a relative change in the electrical and magnetic properties of the propagating medium for the EM wave, usually from air to a partial conductor, the ground for example, is a complex matter.

Figure 2.7 indicates the operation for an incident vertically polarized signal: part of E_i is reflected as E_r, part is transmitted into the ground as E_t. There are also corresponding magnetic vector components of H_i The complex ratio of E_r/E_i can be calculated, as can the other respective ratios.

What is discovered is that the magnitude of E_r/E_i, called the *reflection coefficient,* is a critical function of the angle of incidence, and also the phase of $E_r : E_i$ is likewise a critical function. Also the reflection coefficient is sensitive to the relative conductivity of the ground.

Figure 2.8 shows results suggested by the CCIR, for frequencies of 1 GHz. The results are plotted against the *grazing angle* α shown in Figures 2.6 and 2.7. In general one is looking at radio conditions where a truly grazing angle of reflection applies.

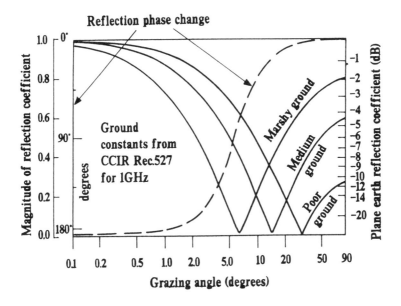

Figure 2.8 Reflection coefficient of a vertically polarized signal for various ground types

Four significant observations can be made

(i)   At grazing angles below about 1° there is good reflection when vertically polarized waves are used.

(ii)   At these low angles the electric vector undergoes a phase reversal of 180°.

(iii) At moderate grazing angles vertically polarized waves are markedly attenuated, but suffer less phase reversal.

(iv)   Horizontally polarized signals do not show the same variation, being generally well reflected, but again with a phase reversal of the reflected component.

In cellular radio one can regard the ground as being horizontal because the distances (cell radii) are generally small, say, in the range of 1-20 km. Thus the grazing angles which apply can be calculated readily from the geometry of Figure 2.6 and the grazing angle is given by

$$\alpha = \tan^{-1} \frac{h_T + h_R}{d} \qquad\qquad (2.16)$$

where h_T and h_R are the effective heights of the BS and MS above the ground plane. Suppose we let $h_T = 30$ m, $h_R = 1$ m, we then find

when d = 300 m α = 5.9°
           = 500 m   = 3.5°
           = 1 km   = 1.8°
           = 3 km   = 0.59°

These results indicate that for very small cells or where the mobile-to-base distance is only a few hundred metres, the ground reflection coefficient may be more complex than we assume below, for example.

2.5 Terrestrial propagation

2.5.1 Simple flat earth model

The usual approach, when dealing with the situation in Figure 2.6, is to assume the distance

$$d \gg h_T \text{ and } h_R$$

which can be shown to give the relative phase delay between the direct ray and the reflected wave as

$$\phi_d = 2 \pi h_T h_R / \lambda d$$

Adding to this the additional phase angle ϕ_r induced by the reflection process, as indicated in Figure 2.8, the electric field received at MS will be the sum of two signals, that is

$$E_S = 2E_R \cos\left(\frac{\phi_r + \phi_d}{2}\right)$$

using the cosine rule, and assuming that the reflection coefficient is unity. If this is the case, and also letting $\phi_r = \pi$ (180°), it then follows that

$$E_S = 2E_R \sin\left(\frac{2\pi h_R h_T}{\lambda d}\right) \qquad (2.17)$$

This result shows that at close distances the field strength will oscillate if h_R or h_T are large, (high), apart from the reflection coefficient problem. Alternatively written as signal strength

$$P_R = 4P_{direct} \cdot \sin^2 [2\pi h_T h_R / \lambda d]$$

in relation to the direct signal level above, and with distances $d > h$ (low angle of incidence), the equation reduces to

$$P_R = 4P_{direct} \cdot [2\pi h_T h_R / \lambda d]^2 \qquad (2.18)$$

Introducing the modified P_R back into (2.11) one now finds

$$P_R/P_T = G_T G_R \cdot [h_T h_R / d^2]^2 \qquad (2.19)$$

Written in logarithmic form the propagation loss thus becomes

$$L_{dB} = 40 \log d_m - 20 \log h_T h_R \qquad (2.20)$$

but where all distances and lengths are in metres.

This equation is of fundamental importance to terrestrial mobile radio. Note especially that it is an inverse *fourth power law* and is independent of frequency. (It is also the basis of CCIR TV and radio coverage data.) The distance d is now in metres, not kilometres, as in the free space equation, and this reminds us that the equation really only applies to small flat earth cells. However, when the operating distance is very small, as it can be in cellular, the above equation, and hence the propagation law, will break down. A signal envelope of the form suggested in Figure 2.9 could be observed.

The fourth power law applies as the mobile moves away from the base site; this implies a 12 dB fall in field strength for every doubling of the distance. Equation (2.20) also indicates that only range d and antenna height affect the signal loss, so the calculation is elementary.

Example (Frequency no longer applicable)

Same distance   d = 1 km = 1000 m
                                 $h_T h_R$ = 10 m² (low antennas)

Therefore   L = 100 dB

Going back to the previous example to calculate P_T, since the loss has added a further 14 dB, making P_T = + 6 dBm, 4 milliwatts is now required for a 1 km radio cell.

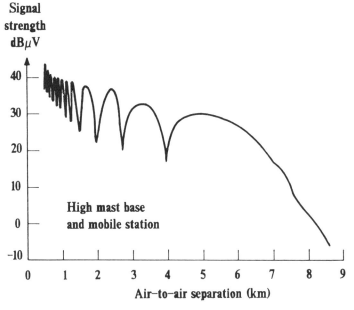

Figure 2.9 Received field strength variation observed because of high BS and close operational distance of MS

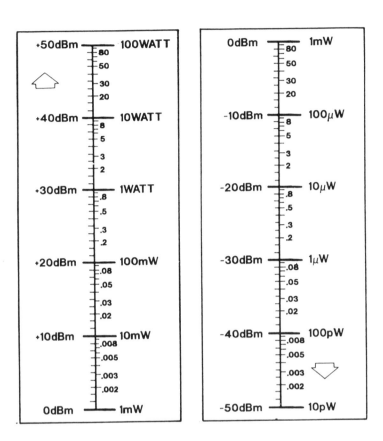

Figure 2.10   Convenient scales for adding, or subtracting dBs to, and from, signal levels
              in dBm

Example   (A larger terrestrial distance)

          Distance   d = 25 km
                      h_T h_R = 100 m² (base station set high)

Therefore   L = 136 dB, i.e. 36 dB worse

The P_T required is now 16 W, seen by reading Figure 2.10.

Observations show that, apart from the ultimate effect of the earth's curva-
ture over a long path (large radio cell), several terrestrial effects must be taken
into account. These include

(i)   Surface roughness
(ii)   Line-of-sight obstacles
(iii) Buildings and trees, etc.
(iv)   Mountainous areas, etc.

The propagation loss equation is therefore amended to read

$$L = 40 \log d - 20 \log h_T h_R + \beta \qquad (2.21)$$

where β is the additional losses, lumped together; these are studied further below. If the *additional loss factor* β is a constant, this equation says that the radio cell (range equal to the radius) is circular. Because β, and h_R, can vary according to which direction one views from the transmitter, radio cells in general are not circular.

2.5.2 Rough ground model

Rough ground conditions are used to indicate the terrain surrounding the base station is not gentle rolling meadows or sandy deserts. We briefly look at computation techniques below, but it is interesting to ask whether some sort of semi-empiral formula is available, i.e. a sort of improved version of Eqn (2.21).

Empirical model formulas are based on force-fitting formulas to measured data. An example for VHF frequencies is

$$L_{dB} = 40 \log d_m - 20 \log h_T h_R + 20 + f/40 + 1.08 L - 0.34H \qquad (2.22)$$

where   f = frequency in MHz
        L = land usage factor - the percentage of the test area covered by buildings of any type
        H = terrain height differences between the T_X and R_X, (R_X terrain height $- T_X$ terrain height)

Example
        f = 160 MHz
        L = 30%
        H = 50 m (over a hill)

Therefore, excess loss, $\beta = 20 + 4 + 6 + 15$
                              $= 45$ dB

This additional 45 dB loss implies that a 125 W base station is now required to cover a path distance, or cell size, of 25 km.

An additional loss factor based on an urbanization factor U can also be introduced. These models are derived with the aid of measurements taken. Actual received signal strength is compared to that predicted by the plane earth equation alone, and the difference (excess clutter factor) found. The final model is therefore composed of the plane earth equation, plus a clutter factor which is a best fit equation based on the factors considered most likely to increase propagation loss.

2.5.3 CCIR standard model

No single model can be expected to fit all conditions and all locations, but the CCIR has suggested a model, based on a long series of observations, known as the CCIR empirical formula for urban areas. It has the following form

$$L_{dB} = 69 + 26 \log f_{MHz} - 14 \log h_T + (45 - 6.5 \log h_T) \log d_{km} - A (h_R) \qquad (2.23)$$

where

$$A(h_R) = (\log f - 0.7) h_R - (1.6 \log f - 0.8)$$

Note the fourth power d law holds exactly for $h_T = 5.9$ m.

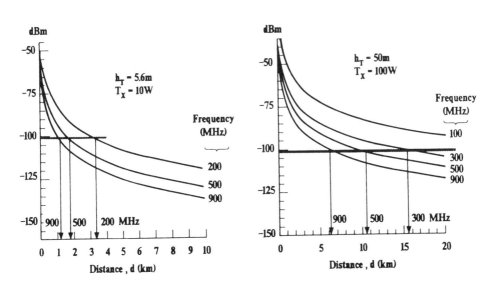

Figure 2.11 Signal strength versus distance according to (2.23). (a) BS height 5.6 m and $P_T = 10$ W (b). BS height 50 m and $P_T = 100$ W; $h_R = 1.5$ m

This equation is plotted as received field strength in Figure 2.11 for various frequencies of operation and assuming the base station powers indicated. By drawing the –101 dBm (50μV/m) threshold line on the signal level scale, some idea of the urban *radio range* can be read off the distance scale.

Figure 2.11(a) is for h_T = 5.6 m (fourth power law). Figure 2.11(b) is for h_T = 50 m, a much higher placed BS. The signal level performance variation close to the BS is clearly not representative, as discussed, but the cell size variation with frequency is well illustrated.

The above empirical model does not consider penetration of radio waves into buildings, nor additional attenuation in major city environments. Figure 2.12 suggests how the signal from the BS might suffer a penetration loss as it radiates into the city environment. The propagation law now changes from d^{-4} to $d^{-n} \times e^{-\alpha(d)}$, where $n \leq 4$ and α is an additional loss factor. The factor α has actually a Gaussian-like distribution, due to the multipath effect (described in Chapter 5, especially Figure 5.1). Taking logs of the modified propagation, in place of a simple fourth power law, one now has

$$L = (10 \times n) \log d + \alpha (d) \qquad\qquad (2.24)$$

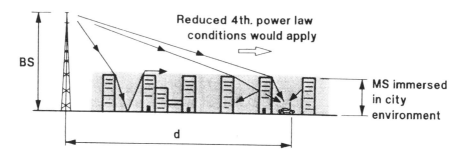

Figure 2.12 Propagation conditions within a city environment

Figure 2.13 indicates some results taken in a Middle East city. Fluctuation of the signal level along the route through the city indicates this scattering absorption and additional loss, particularly for the first kilometre or so, but there is a tendency for the fourth power propagation law to hold up well.

Lee also noticed this and a well known graph of his is shown as Figure 2.14, to which further results have been added. As can be seen from the graph, the more densely built the city, the greater the initial loss factor; e.g. Tokyo shows some 35 dB over an open environment. The general slope of the propagation is perhaps closer to $d^{-3.5}$ law, but we shall use the d^{-4} law in our discussion of cell size in the main.

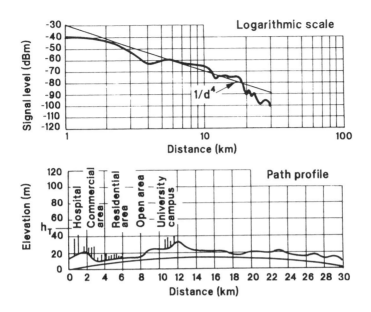

Figure 2.13   Observation of propagation loss (signal level) as MS moves away from a BS in a city environment

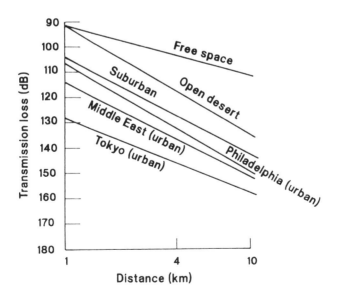

Figure 2.14   Logarithmic plot of the propagation loss for various terrestrial path conditions. The 'free space' result is added for comparison

2.5.4 *Building penetration loss*

Now apart from the additional loss of radio signal in the environment of a congested city (ignoring any strategy for in-fill *picocells* – see Chapters 3 and 10), as a subscriber enters a building, or sits in his car with his handportable, an additional signal loss arises. The *building penetration loss* (BPL) is a matter which has not been fully resolved, because it depends on every imaginable variable associated with building architecture, especially size of the windows, and whether the glass is tinted, etc. The mean signal level will also change with position in a room, and in fact most subscribers know from experience where to stand to make a call. As a rough guide a 10-20 dB reduction of signal level can always be expected. The cellular operator has to make allowance for BPL. in his planning strategy.

2.6 Cell site coverage assessment

A reasonable estimate of the coverage area of a transmitter can be achieved by two means: (i) using a repeater technique (as used in conventional and private land mobile radio systems) will provide an estimate of the radio coverage (cell boundaries) and also does not require the transmitter to be continuously operating; (ii) using a field strength measuring receiver attached to a distance or location monitor. New instruments, handportable or vehicle mounted, can achieve very impressive field strength maps. For digital cellular systems a map showing the bit error rate topography of each cell site is probably more important. This requires sending packets of data over the radio path, say mobile-to-base, and comparing the received data sequence to the expected data in order to determine the BER at the particular location[1]. Poor BER performances do not require long sequences in order to make a measurement, unlike a good BER performance which implies say, at least 100,000 bits of data.

2.7 Computer prediction techniques

For a detailed theoretical field strength prediction, especially for average sized cells, radii from the transmitter (BS) site are laid out on a detailed topographic map of the area (in the UK available from Ordnance Survey). Height data to within 10 m at every 10 m or 50 m intervals, in the form of a grid, can now be purchased from the appropriate authority. Figure 2.15 outlines the concept. Choosing a radial at a specific angle, the ground contour can be averaged from the survey data set out in the form {x, y; h}.

---

[1] In digital cellular, because the speech signal data is sent in frames, the *frame erasure rate* (FER) is actually a more relevant measurement than the average BER.

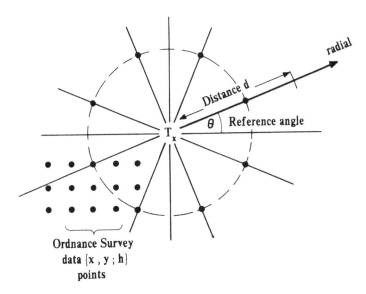

Figure 2.15 Radial lines for planning cell coverage overlaid on topographic data points

If the ground above the radial under consideration is level, or perhaps just urbanized, the signal level path loss formula described above could be used. However, if conditions are hilly, a hill can present a considerable obstacle between a BS and a MS; such as suggested in Figure 2.16.

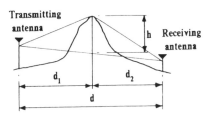

Figure 2.16 Obstacle between transmitter and receiver; the so-called knife edge model

Radio waves do not form an absolute shadow at the other side of an obstacle; rather, zones of radio wave influence are formed in the shadow of the obstacle, known as *Fresnel zones*. Signals found in the shadow and their relative amplitude can be calculated, as depicted in Figure 2.17. The loss is determined by a dimension-less geometric term v, given by

$$v = h \left[\frac{2}{1} \left(\frac{1}{d_1} + \frac{1}{d_2} \right) \right]^{1/2} \qquad (2.25)$$

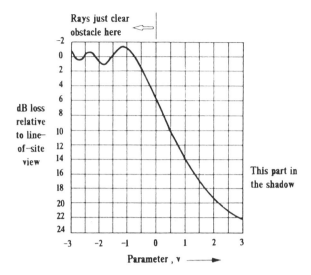

Figure 2.17 The additional loss due to an obstacle in the path of a radial

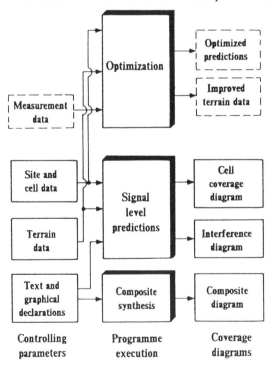

Figure 2.18   Management arrangement within a computerized cell site radio coverage
              programme

Clearly UHF is more affected by such obstacles because λ is smaller, etc. The results can be fed automatically into computerized field strength programs when and where such an obstacle appears along a radial. A typical program structure is shown in Figure 2.18. The functions discussed above will be recognized, and supported by a composite diagram. In addition, two important additional features are the calculation of signals from possible surrounding cells, and also the optimization of the terrain data and model prediction by force-fitting to measured data, as described above.

Illustration of a cell site prediction is usually made in colour – the colours being used to show where the field strength lies between –85 and –90 dBm, for example. Composite diagrams showing the coverage offered to subscribers are now a very familiar offering; the coverage from any BS is now hidden in the overall plan. Around the coastline of countries bordering the sea, semi-circular coverage will be noticed, because the coverage will be circular. Inland, of course, the local terrain characterizes the pattern very much.

2.8 Typical cell coverage findings

Table 2.1 Cell sizes for the various cellular systems deduced by noting bandwidth and propagation laws described

System	C/N for noise level $kT_oB + 10\ dB$ $= NF + 10\ dB$ dB	Total path loss allowable with BS EIRP $= +40\ dBm\ (10W)$	Cell size for $d^{-3.5}$ law $+ 20\ dB$ loss radius (km)
AMPS	−109	149	4.85
TACS	−110	150	5.18
NMT	−113	153	6.31
GSM	−101	141	2.86
D-AMPS	−109	149	4.85
CDMA	−93	133	1.69

As a recapitulation on the above discussion of what is really quite a complex subject, namely coverage prediction, it is useful perhaps to group together the key features which have been introduced. To some extent, most matters are contained within Eqn 2.14. For example, one needs to achieve a minimum C/N ratio, which defines the maximum cell radius. In Table 2.1 we have assumed that we need C/N = +10 dB with the noise level dictated by the system bandwidth. (In column 2, we have used the receiver bandwidth equal to the system bandwidth plus 10%, e.g. AMPS = 30 kHz + 10% = 33 kHz = + 45 dBHz.) Then we must add a figure for receiver site noise; we have taken this to be NF = + 10 dB, e.g. see Figure 2.5.

Now, choosing a BS (or MS) EIRP, one can use Eqn 2.14 to work out the maximum sustainable propagation loss. (The EIRP can take in the antenna gain at the BS for the MS, or antenna loss, at the MS for the BS, and so a value of EIRP = + 40 dBm is not a bad starting figure.) The values of L calculated are listed as column 3.

To work out the corresponding range one could use Eqn 2.20. However, the subsequent discussion concerning build-up areas suggests that a $d^{3.5}$ loss law might be more applicable, e.g. Figure 2.14, and also there is often a starting loss; we have assumed 20 dB. Column 4 then lists the conceptual range. What is significant is the influence of system bandwidth, which is discussed more in later chapters. To look at other scenarios, one can just add or subtract dBs and double the distance for a gain of 10 dB, or vice versa.

Further reading

CCIR (1982). *Recommendations and reports, XV Plenary Assembly,* Geneva, Volume V, (Propagation in non-ionized media)

Edwards, R. and Durking, J. (1969). 'Computer prediction of service areas for VHF mobile radio networks', *Proc IEE,* 116, Sept, pp 1493-1500

Griffiths, J. (1987). *Radio Wave Propagation and Antennas,* Prentice Hall International Ltd, UK

IEEE Vech Tech report on propagation (1988). 'Coverage prediction for mobile radio systems operating in the 800/900 MHz frequency range', *IEEE Veh Tech,* VT-37, Feb, pp 3-70

Lee, W.C.Y. (1982). *Mobile Communications Engineering,* McGraw-Hill Book Co, USA

Parsons, J.D. (1992). *The Mobile Radio Propagation Channel,* Pentech Press, London, UK

3 Cellular Radio Design Principles

3.1 Analog cellular frequency allocation plans

In its simplest concept radiotelephones are set up by assigning one pair of channels to each user or phone. As in broadcasting, a channel is defined by its centre frequency and bandwidth. This scheme is known as frequency division multiplexing (FDM) and works very well. It is the basis of all present day analog cellular schemes. This channel planning concept is shown in Figure 3.1.

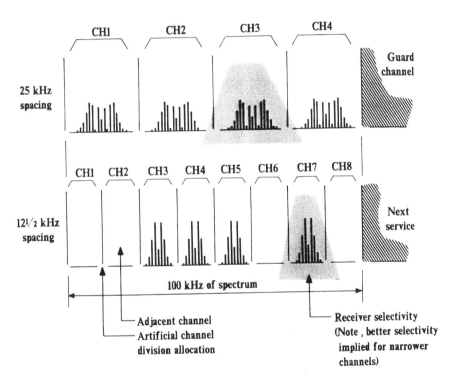

Figure 3.1 Channel arrangement within a 100 kHz band of spectrum: four 25 kHz channels, or eight 12.5 kHz channels are possible

This plan shows, either the spectrum at the base station transmitter, or the spectrum seen by the mobile station receiver. For duplex operation, the mobile also needs to transmit and the base station receive (on multiple receivers). In order to avoid the receiver's seeing the same transmitted frequency, or the base receiver for a distant mobile being interfered by the transmission from a nearby mobile, the transmit and receiver frequencies must be well separated. The frequency difference between the channel pairs is usually 45 MHz, and is within the performance capability of the duplexer shown in the mobile circuit outline drawn earlier as Figure 1.3. The channel carrier spacing is normally 25 kHz, at least in the UK.

A simplified view of the band plan for the UK TACS system is shown in Figure 3.2. The radio spectrum assigned is basically 890-915 and 935-960 MHz. This therefore allows one thousand channels for the service. The forward paths are the higher frequencies (because as we noted in Chapter 2 higher frequencies have slightly more propagation loss) and refer to the BS transmit frequencies. The return paths are the lower frequencies and refer to the MS transmitter frequencies. Since the edge of this band is 890 MHz, the actual first transmit frequency specified will be 890.0125 MHz, i.e. 12.5 kHz up from 890 MHz, as explained by Figure 3.1. Likewise, considering channel 27 for example, which is actually allocated as a beacon channel of the base station, the signal here will appear on the frequency

$$F_{27} = 935 + 26 \times 0.025 + 0.0125$$
$$= 935.6625 \text{ MHz}$$

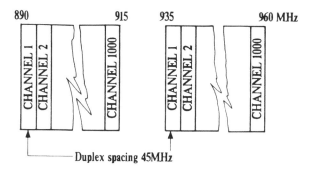

Figure 3.2 Outline allocation for TACS frequencies and channels

The channel assignment is actually made more complicated as a *duopoly* of operators is allowed access to the radio spectrum channels. Calling the two operators A and B respectively, an arrangement for sharing can be illustrated by reference to the USA AMPS assignments, Figure 3.3. The frequency limits are not the same as indicated in Figure 3.2 (the global regional variation principle described in Chapter 1), nor is the channel bandwidth the same; 30 kHz is employed by AMPS. The result is that one has (the original) 666 channels, plus 166 additional channels from a further assigned 5 MHz of spectrum. Note that the channel numbering scheme goes up to CH799, then stops, and begins again at the lower frequencies for CH991 to CH1023. The control channels, twenty-one per operator, go from channels 313–333 and 334–354, respectively. It is also worth noting that if there is only one operator, only the A channels would be deployed, for example. A second operator could come on stream on the B channels (even directly with a D-AMPS service if this was the decided strategy).

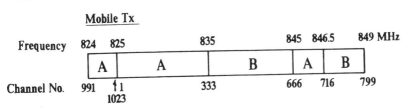

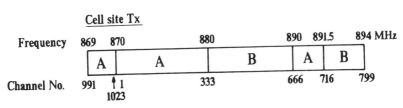

Figure 3.3 Current AMPS channel allocation arrangement

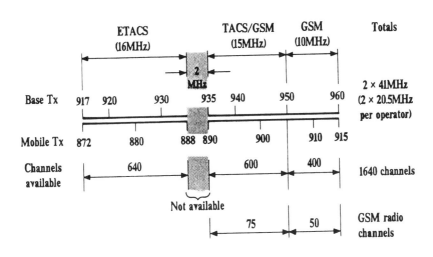

Figure 3.4 Spectrum allocation to cellular in the UK (DCS 1800 band not included)

The allocation of spectrum to cellular radio in the UK, at present, is shown in Figure 3.4. Notable differences from Figure 3.2 are worth highlighting. Firstly, extended TACS, or ETACS, provides a further 320 channels per operator (Vodafone and Cellnet), by going to the lower frequency limits of 917 and 872 MHz, respectively. On the other hand, the top 10 MHz of each band is now assigned to the scheduled pan-European digital cellular network (GSM), so the upper bounds are now 950 and 905 MHz respectively, not the same as in Figure 3.2.

Again, it needs to be recalled that a number of channels need to be dedicated as control channels. Like AMPS, twenty-one are assigned per operator; for TACS, these are channels 23 to 43 and 323 to 343 respectively.

The frequency arrangements of other services are listed in Chapter 9 regarding the newer higher frequency services.

3.2 Base station site engineering

It will be clear that the mobile unit will have to be very frequency agile and also carry an antenna which can both receive and transmit over a fairly wide band of frequencies; that is, the antenna must be broadband especially with regard to its *voltage standing wave ratio* (VSWR) on transmit.

Any base station at a particular cell site will have a very different task, however; not only will it be receiving many signals, channel by channel, it will also need the capability of transmitting simultaneously on many separate channels, though not quite as adjacent as in Figure 3.1. As we shall note later, digital cellular radio minimizes this particular problem to some extent (at the expense of another), but this multiplicity of operation is a very real requirement.

Although separate common transmit and receive antennas could be used at the base station, with gain especially on the return path, because the two antennas would be in close proximity, they could to all intents and purposes be regarded as one, due to the close coupling involved. To separate the signals a methodology known as antenna site engineering is used, see Figure 3.5.

Spectrum dividing filters, as shown, differentiate between the forward and return channel bands. Each transmitter would have an associated multicoupler in order that there was no return transmitted power, between the channelized transmitters. The BS receivers would have to have a very linear common pre-amplifier, to ensure low intermodulation between very unequally sized received carriers, and a low noise figure.

The channels in use at any particular base station will not be adjacent channels, but separated according to the cell cluster pattern arrangements described below.

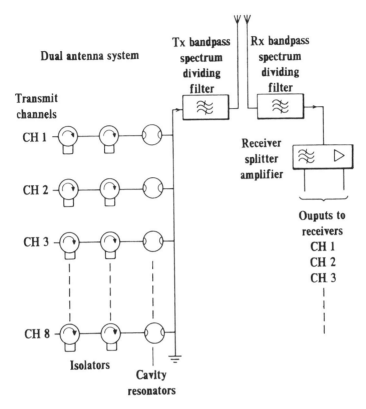

Figure 3.5 Outline of base station antenna site components

3.3 The concept and benefits of channel sharing

The combination of the mobile station being frequency agile and the allocation of many channels in a band means that each mobile has *access* to many channels. In analog cellular this is on a channel-by-channel basis, termed FDMA; in digital cellular described later, a band-by-band allocation is used and is termed narrowband TDMA.

Figure 3.6 illustrates the arrangement which applies both to the forward and to the return path between the BS and MS. Two observations may be made; firstly, more subscribers than channels appears to be possible, especially if each call (message) is short and the subscribers make use of the network randomly. This is known as the principle of *trunking*; demonstrated by the drawing in Figure 3.7. The principle of trunking comes from telephony and is a scheme which allows the subscribers to have access to all available channels and hence have a many-fold increase in the likelihood of a successful connection. A figure for the trunking gain can be calculated when facts about the subscriber traffic behaviour are known, see Chapter 11.

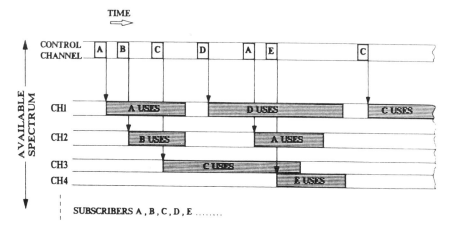

Figure 3.6 Demand allocation of voice channels

Figure 3.7 A conceptual view of trunking gain

In a trunked scheme a larger number of mobiles can be given a more acceptable grade of service than could be supported on an equivalent number of single channel systems. Conversely, the same number of mobiles on single channel systems could be given a better grade of service on a trunked system; or, the same number of mobiles could be given the same grade of service on fewer channels.

This thus saves the number of channels needed. The reliability of the system is also very much greater. The loss of one base station channel merely degrades the service; to a single channel user this would mean the total loss of communication.

We need to define *grade of service* (GOS). This is a measure of the probability that a successful connection (a call) will not be achieved (a somewhat back to front definition). Telephone companies look for a GOS in the range of value 0.01; implying that only one call in 100 is lost. This is a theory very much at the heart of telephone traffic performance and is described in more detail in Chapter 10. For the present we just need to accept the obvious advantage of many channels sharing, or trunking, as depicted in Figures 3.6 and 3.7. To put numbers on the gain requires much theory and assumptions.

The second point from Figures 3.6 is that the operation of a control channel is needed to manage the channel (frequency) allocation as requested by each MS. This leads to the complicated issue of signalling in the cellular network (next chapter), but also one notes that the control channel could itself become blocked, due to over use, and hence limit the number of subscribers entering a radio cell even if it were allocated a large quantity of voice channels.

Clearly, channels must be allocated with a minimum of delay. In some specifications, 1200 bps fast frequency shift keying has been chosen as a compromise between speed and reliability within a 12.5 kHz channel separation. The TACS cellular system employs 8 kbps direct modulation. (A channel separation of 50 kHz is now needed to accommodate this.)

The protocol used must ensure full reliability of correct connection in the mobile environment. The signalling telegrams themselves have powerful error-detection capability so that significant falsings will not occur. However, many messages are likely to be rejected in bad signal conditions and therefore the protocol must be designed around acknowledgements and retries. A balance between no retries and an excessive number must be agreed which does not overload the control channel, but in cellular the traffic channels are usually limiting because no limit on conversation length is applied.

The inclusion of queuing in a system design is of interest. If a system has become very busy the only means of access to a traffic channel, if there is no queuing, is by continuous retries. This may be accomplished manually or automatically or by a combination of both. These retries will tend to block the control channel and at the moment a traffic channel becomes available contention could be so great as to require time to reallocate it. This reduces the efficiency of the system and could generate frustration to the user. Secondly, the user may have a more favourable perception of the system when he obtains a queued message. Also, emergency and priority calls can be more readily processed.

Notice that a certain amount of privacy is built into the frequency agile FDMA technique, because it is not known on which channel a particular subscriber may appear. Also the system can be expanded by adding more channels at a particular cell site, if necessary.

To recapitulate, in any cellular system the operation has recourse to a great many voice channels at a particular location, the more so, the more channels appear to be on offer because of the trunking gain. However, once the channels (or frequencies) have been allocated, they are not available; the subscriber has to move to another site, or wait. This brings us to the principle of cell planning which we shall now discuss.

3.4 Multiple cell plan

The basic shortcoming of the single large radio site is the imbalance of power levels at the centre and the edge of the cell. For example, suppose one could cover a 1 mile radius cell with a 100 mW transmitter power. To cover a 10 mile radius cell would require 100 W transmitter power – because of the inverse fourth power propagation law alone.

The only way to achieve coverage with lower powers is to arrange coverage with a subset of small cells, as in Figure 3.8.

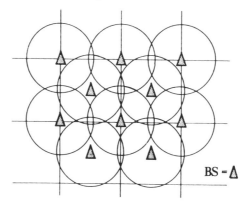

Figure 3.8 Radio cells laid out on a national grid network. (This arrangement is used for the European terrestrial flight (cellular) telephone system, for example.)

The cellular concept was described in some detail in Chapter 1; Figure 3.8 shows a more practical layout arrangement, at least over a geographically flat area. There is a good deal of overlap of coverage, but this does not matter too much since a different set of frequencies is used in each cell. In fact with the development of high capacity digital cellular, cell overlap becomes a real and necessary matter, so that present day cell planning comes closer to this diagram than the academic schemes to be now described.

However, it is clear from the overlaid drawing of a regular hexagon and a circle in Figure 3.9 that the hexagonal shape is a much more attractive geometrical shape to use for planning multiple cells than a circle. Other possible geometric shapes are triangles (used by broadcasters) and squares. in each of these cases the shapes can be 'tessellated', that is, fitted together exactly.

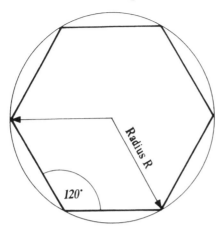

Figure 3.9 The regular hexagon coverage area as compared to a circle. The cell radius R
            is indicated

3.4.1 Cell structure geometry

Hexagons may be packed side-by-side (no overlap necessary) and examination
of a set of hexagons shows that they can be packed in *clusters* such that no two
similar cells are adjacent, i.e. use the same set of frequencies. The *cluster size* is
designated by the letter N. N is determined by the condition:

$$N = i^2 + ij + j^2$$

where i, j = 0, 1, 2, etc.

Thus only the cluster sizes 3, 4, 7, 9, 12, etc, are possible, at least in a regular
pattern of cells. It is actually possible to change the value of N to other integers
by 'skewing' the pattern, but the operational value of such techniques, compared to cell frequency assignment strategies, reduces the value of the concept.

  The standard repeat patterns are illustrated in Figure 3.10. An individual cell
may also be sectored, in particular by 120°, as evident from the geometry of
Figure 3.9. This means that a 9 cell cluster can also be regarded as 3 clusters of
9 sectored cells, called a 3/9 cell cluster. Other examples are shown in Figure
3.10. Note also that in a normal cluster, the BS is at the centre of each cell. In
the sectored arrangement the BS is at the edge of the cells, and the BS antenna
would be made directional, as described in Chapter 2.

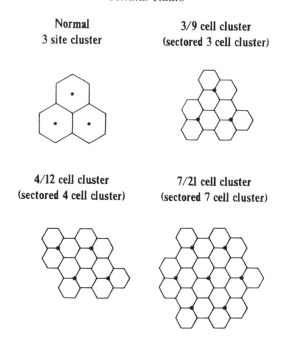

Figure 3.10   Cellular repeat patterns. The base station locations are indicated by the
black dots

3.4.2 Reuse distance

The cell cluster size has two significant attributes. Thus if one focuses on the
popular 7-cell cluster arrangement, redrawn in Figure 3.11, it is firstly noticed
that the allocation of frequencies into seven sets is required. Thus if 210
frequencies were available, this would mean that only 30 channels per cell
could be assigned, one or more of which would be needed as a control channel,
so that at least 14 control channels would not be available as traffic channels in
the cluster. For duplex operation this pattern is repeated in the two allocated
bands.

The second important aspect of Figure 3.11 is the mean distance between
cells using the same frequency set. This is called the *mean reuse distance* D.
Because of the geometry of hexagons, D is related to the cell radius R, and the
ratio of D to R, called the *reuse ratio,* is a function of cluster size, and

$$\frac{D}{R} = \sqrt{3N}$$

(3.1)

Thus for a 7-cell cluster of 2-mile radius cells, the repeat cell centre would be 9.2 miles away.

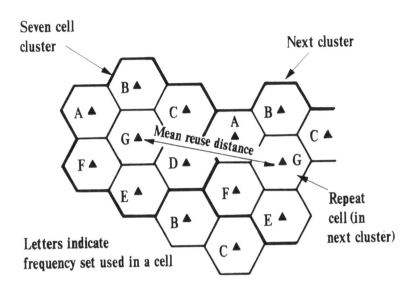

Figure 3.11 Seven-cell repeat pattern showing the mean reuse distance between cells

The distance away of a similar on-frequency transmitter will cause *co-channel interference* to a mobile in its rightful cell. For a 7-cell cluster there could be up to six immediate interferers, as shown in Figure 3.12.

Assuming the fourth power propagation law, an approximate value of the carrier C to interference I ratio is

$$\frac{C}{I} = \frac{C}{\sum 6I's} = \frac{R^{-4}}{6D^{-4}}$$

assuming that the interferers contribute equally.

Using $D/R = (3N)^{\frac{1}{2}}$

$$\therefore \frac{C}{I} = \frac{1}{6}(3N)^2 = 1.5N^2 \tag{3.2}$$

i.e. the C/I ratio is a function of the cluster size; it is designated C_i. (Note that the result is an approximation for values other than interferers = 6, and also, of course, for other propagation laws, but is adequate for the discussions which follow.)

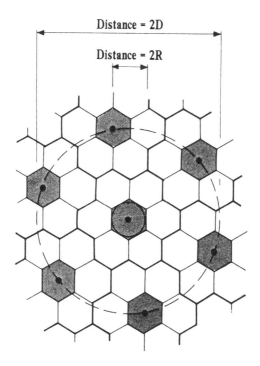

Figure 3.12   The geometry associated with interfering cells using a 7–cell cluster
              pattern

Example   Suppose N = 7,
                then C = 73 or 18 dB.

This appears very adequate, but two other facts have to be taken into account:

(i)   *Adjacent channel interference* from channels in adjacent neighbouring
      cells. This is worse in small cell clusters.

(ii) *Multipath fading* may weaken C as against I, discussed later.

   However, it is useful at this stage to draw up a table comparing the properties
of various cluster sites. This is shown as Table 3.1.
   From this table one can also plot the number of channels per cluster and the
C/I ratio versus cluster size N, and note the step function nature of the result,
shown in Figure 3.13.

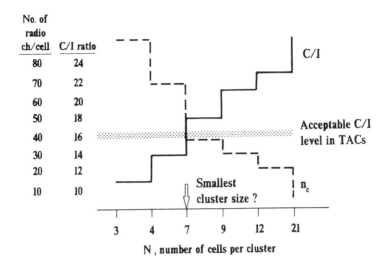

Figure 3.13   Number of radio channels per cell (out of 300) and C/I ratio (dB) plotted against cell cluster size N

Table 3.1 Influence of cluster size on individual cell parameters

Cluster size N	(a) reuse ratio	(b) max no. of CH per cell	(c) co-channel C_i (dB)	(d) no. of subs per cell
3	3	93	11	2583
4	3.5	69	14	1840
7	4.6	39	18	937
9	5.2	31	21	707
12	6	23	23	483
21	7.9	14	28	245

(a) using (3.1)

(b) 300 channels per operator assumed available, of which 21 must be control channels

(c) using (3.2)

(d) for calculation here, see Chapter 10, section 5.2.

The parameters shown in the Table 3.1 are independent of the cell size R, which is assumed to have the *same value* for all cells in the cell plan. The actual reuse distance will depend on the value of R chosen, i.e. for 2 km cells, the second column is only half the reuse distance in km. The third column depends on the frequency allocation plan, and applies more or less to AMPS and TACS. The C_i ratio is in decibels in the fourth column and is independent of cell size. Large cells fare no better than small cells, which at first sight does seem strange, but of course large cells need more effective and positioned radiated power. The final column requires calculation of the trunking gain, which is postponed until Chapter 10. The figures assume a grade of service of 0.01 and an average calling rate of the individual subscribers. The advantage of small cluster sizes is clearly necessary in the centre of large busy cities.

In the UK TACS system, N was initially chosen as 7 or 12 because of C_i considerations. With 300 channels available per operator, of which 21 were dedicated as control channels, this leaves the 39 or 23 channels per cell, respectively.

3.4.3 Adjacent channel interference

The spectral overhang components of analog FM were indicated in Figure 3.1, while an example from digital cellular is shown in Figure 6.19. Both the MS and the BS receiver IF selectivity performance will tend to cancel the adjacent channel spectral components, but because of the near-far problems in the cellular mobile scenario, the differential propagation path loss can add a very large number of dBs to the ACI signals compared to the on-channel signal. The best that one can do is to keep adjacent channels as far apart as possible. A popular scheme for a GSM network is shown in Figure 3.21 where base station sitings are discussed. The voice channels in cells are chosen to be far away from those in their adjacent cells, from the channel set available in the frequency plan, because of *adjacent channel interference* (ACI) and bandwidth overlap problems.

3.4.4 Cell splitting

For a given value of N, the capacity of a system may be increased by reducing the size of the cells so that the total number of *channels available per unit area* is increased. In practice this is achieved by the process of 'cell splitting', where new base stations are established at specific points in the cellular pattern, reducing the cell size by a factor of 3 or 4. By repeatedly splitting cells, the system capacity can be tailored to meet the traffic capacity requirements demanded by customers, in areas, from low traffic rural areas, say, where the cells may be 10 km radius or more, to high traffic central urban areas, say, where cells may be as small as 1 km radius. In practice, the variation in propagation, particularly in urban centres, and the accuracy in position to which base stations can be located, are factors limiting the minimum cell size, particular in analog cellular. Digital systems allow a closer packing, and also a multilayer cell plan arrangement to be put in place, as described later.

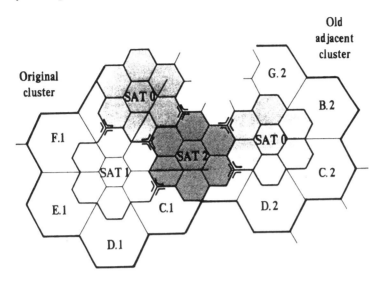

Figure 3.14 Cell splitting procedure

An example of cell splitting is shown in Figure 3.14. When this exercise is carried out the *colour code* (DCC) and the *supervisory audio tone* (SAT) coding of the newly created clusters must also be revised. This was discussed to some extent in Chapter 1, in particular Figure 1.15. There are three SAT tones; keeping the centre of the original cluster with its original SAT tone, Figure 3.14 indicates which tones are applied to the new smaller clusters. Similar considerations will also apply to the digital colour codes (DCC) of which there are four.

3.4.5 Sectorization

Although in theory, as the cells are split into smaller sizes, the interference received from reuse cells, indicated in Figure 3.12 and Table 3.1 would remain the same, irregular propagation in dense urban areas, and non-circular cell shapes, leads to increasing interference being received from the surrounding cells all using the same channel set. One way of reducing the level of interference is to use directional antennas at base stations, with each antenna illuminating a sector of the cell, and with a separate channel set allocated to each sector. There are two commonly used methods of sectorization, either using three 120° sectors or six 60° sectors, both of which reduce the number of prime interference sources. The three sector case is generally used with a seven-cell repeat pattern, giving an overall requirement for 21 channel sets, as shown in Figure 3.10. The improved co-channel rejection in the six sector case, however, particularly the rejection of secondary interferers, results in a four-cell repeat pattern being possible, but needs an overall requirement of 24 channel sets.

A disadvantage of sectorization is that the larger number of channel sets required results in fewer channels per sector, and thus a reduction in trunking efficiency. This means that the total traffic which can be carried for a given grade of service is reduced. However, the capability to use much smaller cells through sectorization outweighs such drawbacks, and the end result can be a higher capacity system.

3.4.6 Other cell patterns

The overlaid cell concept is shown in Figure 3.15. It allows further reuse of frequencies at each site, provided that they are only used by mobiles within a smaller radius than that of the macrocell, thus providing additional capacity at the centre of a cell. It is important that the cell site is located where the peak traffic occurs. The overlaid cells use frequency groups that are already allocated to normal adjacent macrocells. The reuse distance for the overlaid cell appropriate to a seven-cell cluster can thus be maintained and hence the quality of service is approximately the same as that of the main cell plan.

For illustration, the London cell plan as was used by the UK Vodafone network is shown in Figure 3.16. This illustrates the use of the techniques just described to achieve adequate traffic capacity. (The diagram should be compared to Figure 1.7.) It demonstrates how cell layout strategy needs to develop in order to meet increasing numbers of subscribers on the network ; in London it is now easily approaching a million per operator.

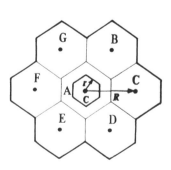

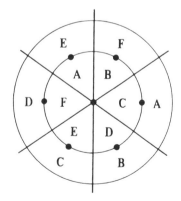

Figure 3.15 An overlaid cell arrangement   Figure 3.17 The Stockholm ring plan and
                                                            the first expansion pattern

Both TACS and AMPS are not particularly good in respect of adjacent channel interference because the signalling tones (see next chapter) are fast frequency shift keying waveforms with a high deviation and, as discussed in Chapter 6, the modulated waveform adjacent channel spectrum is not well controlled. This is not the case with the lower deviation, slower speed signalling systems such as NMT 450 and NMT 900 (see Table 4.2). A cell layout strategy known as the Stockholm ring can be employed. The central site can now have access to all the available channels which are sectored in 60° co-sited sectors.

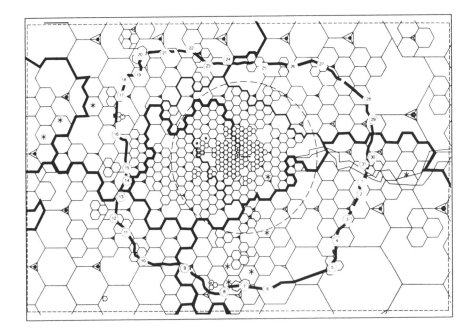

Figure 3.16 1992 Vodafone London cell plan arrangement

Expansion away from the centre is demonstrated by Figure 3.17. This strategy could well be suitable for the walled European Roman type of city, such as Avignon in France, Chester in England and Solothurn in Switzerland. If a large number of channels are available to the cellular service being contemplated, a hexagonal layout pattern is most likely to be employed however, as expansion into the surrounding rural areas becomes simpler. The cell shape, called cell pulling, can also be effected by changing the handover parameters, discussed later. As perhaps could be ascertained from Figure 3.8, this is a strategy of assigning the region of overlap between cells to one or the other cell, hence reshaping the layout pattern. This option is under the command of the switching centre that oversees a particular cluster of cells.

3.5 The cellular system

The basic concepts of frequency planning and reuse, and the control of co-channel interference, are equally applicable to private mobile radio systems and indeed also apply to TV and radio broadcasting. What is different with cellular is that the individual base stations are interconnected to form a complete system, offering continuous coverage with a minimum user inconvenience. There are two key features of cellular systems which make this possible, mobile location and in-call handover.

3.5.1 Mobile location

When an incoming call is received for a mobile station, the call has to be routed to the cell where the mobile is located so that the call can be connected. One way of finding the mobile would be to transmit a calling message (page) for the mobile on every cell site in the network. However, with hundreds of cells and hundreds of thousands of mobiles, the signalling capacity required would clearly be astronomical. Instead the cellular network is split up into a number of location areas, each with its own area identity number. This number is then transmitted regularly from all base stations in the area as part of the system's control information. A mobile station, when not engaged in a call, will lock on to the control channel of the nearest base station and, as it moves about the network, will from time to time select a new base station to lock on to. The mobile station will check the area identity number transmitted by the base station, and when it detects a change, indicating that the mobile has moved to a new location area, it will automatically inform the network of its new location by means of a signalling interchange with the base station.

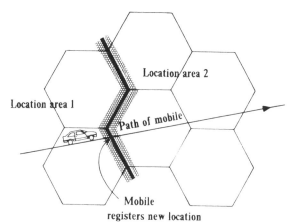

Figure 3.18 Mobile location registration

In this way, the network can keep a record (registration) of the current location area of each mobile, and therefore be able to call the mobile only within that area. Also, because a particular control channel frequency is assigned to each location area or cell in a cluster, each cell is actually numbered in the network. This becomes more obvious when describing digital cellular.

3.5.2 *In call handover*

The description below applies particularly to analog operation. Appreciating the (simpler) strategy used here acts as a useful introduction to the more complex digital strategies described later.

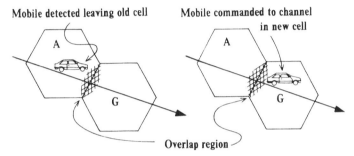

Figure 3.19 In call handover operation

When a mobile station is engaged in a call, it will frequently move out of the coverage area of the base station with which it is in communication, and unless the call is passed on to another cell, it will be lost. The system continuously monitors the signals received from mobiles engaged in calls, checking on signal strength (and quality). When the signal falls below a preset threshold the system will check whether any other base station can receive the mobile at better strength and, if this is the case, the system will allocate a channel for the call at the new base station, and the mobile will be commanded by a signalling message to switch to the new frequency. The whole process of measurement, channel allocation and handover may take a few seconds to complete, but the user will only notice a break in conversation of 200-300 ms as the handover itself is carried out.

Effective and reliable handover is not only highly desirable from the user's point of view, but essential in the control of co-channel interference and maintenance of the cell plan, particularly as the cell size is reduced. A mobile operating in a non-optimum cell will, in effect, be operating outside the cell designated for that area. In other words, the cell boundary will have been altered beyond its planned limit, and this will give rise to levels of co-channel interference above that planned for the adjacent system.

A further means to control co-channel interference is that of mobile power control. So long as the base station is receiving a signal of adequate strength from a mobile, there is no need for the mobile to be transmitting extra power. The base station can command the mobile to reduce power by sending a signalling message. Clearly, by reducing a mobile's power, the likelihood of its causing interference is also reduced, thus helping to control interference levels.

The radiated power of the base station is kept constant, however, since this defines the cell size. The cell edge signal strength for AMPS/TACS follows recommendations based on experience. These are:

For AMPS receiver sensitivity = −116 dBm for a 12 dB SINAD
(Using Eqn 2.5 this suggests 12 μV/m at the antenna).
For TACS the value of −113 dBm, corresponding to a 20 dB SINAD, is suggested; the point at which handover would be activated.

3.6 The cellular network

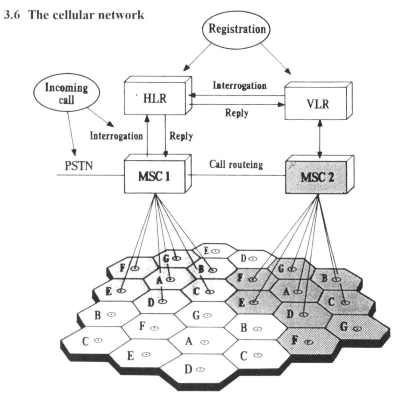

Figure 3.20   A conceptual diagram of the fixed network supporting the cellular radio
              layout

In essence, all cellular networks have a similar structure, being complete telephone networks in their own right, with dedicated exchanges within an interconnected network, and with base stations connected to the exchanges. There are, however, many ways of planning a cellular network in practice, the optimum arrangement for any particular application being dependent upon the capacity required, cost of implementation, capabilities of the chosen manufacturer's equipment, etc. As an illustration of the network design, Figure 3.20 shows sets of seven-cluster cells connected in turn to their command centre, that is MSC. Each mobile switching centre will have a home location register (HLR) and visitor location register (VLR) associated with it, as described in the introductory chapter.

3.6.1 Base stations

For many networks, base stations are organized in a 7-cell or 12-cell repeat pattern with omnidirectorial coverage from each base station. Most base stations have between 20 and 30 voice channels, with one signalling channel carrying all paging and access functions are per cell. The signalling or control channel transmitters and receivers are fully redundant, both operating in a work/standby mode. Voice channels are non-redundant, and any faulty channels can be taken out of service, only slightly worsening the grade of service of the cell.

The voice channel and signalling channel transmitter outputs are combined using high-Q cavity resonators and fed to co-linear antennas of 9 dB gain. The maximum effective radiated power (ERP) of each channel used to be 100 W, but in most cases a lower power level is used, as dictated by the co-channel interference requirements of the overall radio plan.

In the receive direction, many base stations are fitted with six directional antennas consisting of a colinear type mounted in front of a vertical corner reflector. These antennas have 17 dB gain, and are mounted at 60° intervals around the compass, starting at due north. A preselector/preamplifier is connected to each antenna and the six outputs are connected to a switching matrix which allows any one of the voice channel receivers to use any pair of antennas at any time. A pair of antennas is connected to the voice channel receiver, so that diversity can be used to minimize the effects of fading on the received signal (see Chapter 5).

In order that the best antenna is always connected to each voice channel, the base station has a scanning receiver which monitors the signal level on every channel used by the base station, via every antenna, every few seconds. The results of these measurements are then used by the base station controller to operate the antenna switching matrix. The scanning receiver also carries out measurements of signal strength for both hand-in and hand-out from the cell and for mobile power control. Like the signalling transceiver, both scanning receiver and base station controller are fully redundant.

Using directional antennas for receiving, even when the base station has a nominal omnidirectorial coverage, brings a number of advantages. The high antenna gain and the use of diversity improves receive performance, particularly for handportables, compensating for the power difference between base station and mobile. Co-channel interference in the mobile-to-base station direction is reduced because the base station is only looking one way, and therefore seeing fewer interferers. Also, handover processing is improved since the system can establish the direction of the mobile from the current base station, and therefore indicate more closely the next best cell for handover.

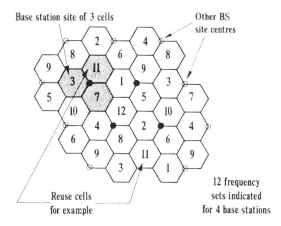

Figure 3.21 Frequency plan for a 4 × 3 reuse pattern

In urban areas, particularly large cities, where customer numbers and usage demand a very high capacity service, base stations can be arranged in a four-cell repeat pattern with six sectors per cell. Each of the six sectors in a four-cell cluster is allocated its own set of voice channels. Control channels, however, are allocated on a one-per-base-station basis, with one signalling channel transceiver in the base station operating as a resource shared by the six sectors. When a mobile initiates a call, the base station controller establishes in which sector's coverage area the mobile is located, and allocates a voice channel in that sector. During a call, if the mobile moves to a different sector, the base station controller can within a few seconds carry out a sector-to-sector handover to ensure that the mobile is being covered by the best sector.

Digital cellular, which is more robust in the face of co-channel interference, in general, uses a 4 × 3 reuse pattern. This pattern is shown in Figure 3.21, basically the same as Figure 3.10, but now including the surrounding cells, i.e. what we have been calling sectors. The cells in a particular cluster are numbered 1-12. From the numbers, the reuse distance $D = (3 \times 12)^{\frac{1}{2}} R = 6 R$, can be appreciated and also how the traffic channel frequencies can be allocated by examining Table 3.2.

Table 3.2 RF channel allocation for a 4 × 3 reuse pattern

Cell number	1	2	3	4	5	6	7	8	9	10	11	12
Carrier number	f_1	f_2	f_3	f_4	f_5	f_6	f_7	f_8	f_9	f_{10}	f_{11}	f_{12}
	f_{13}	f_{14}	f_{15}	f_{16}	f_{17}	f_{18}	f_{19}	f_{20}	f_{21}	f_{22}	f_{23}	f_{24}

Two traffic channels per cell are always allocated (needing a total of 24 channels), but by using an upper/lower band strategy, good adjacent channel separation is also achieved.

3.6.2 *Mobile switching centres*

A national switching network can consist of over many (10's) of mobile switching centres, but in fewer locations. The MSCs are digital exchanges with a distributed control architecture, especially adapted for operation in the cellular environment. One MSC is often marked as the principle MSC, called the *anchor MSC*. Others, which have a connection to the PSTN are *gateway MSCs* (GMSC).

Base stations are connected to the switching centres by digital (2 Mbps) leased lines. The switching centres are also linked together with digital circuits forming a fully interconnected network. The signalling between base stations and switches, and between switches, is often proprietary in nature, and is carried in time slots on the digital circuits.

GMSCs connect to the PSTN at several locations in order to distribute the traffic load and to minimize the impact of any failures on call handling. Digital interconnection to the PSTN using the CCITT signalling system No. 7 is used exclusively, having completely replaced the earlier digital/analog interconnect with loop-disconnect signalling, as existed in earlier fixed telephone networks.

3.7 Connecting the network

The *public land mobile network* (PLMN), outlines of which were shown in Figures 1.8 and 3.20, needs telecommunication connection, particularly between the many cell sites, BSCs and the MSCs. The most common form of transmission link is microwave radio. Microwave dishes can be noticed on even the loneliest cell site, or attached to sites used by several operators, and so on.

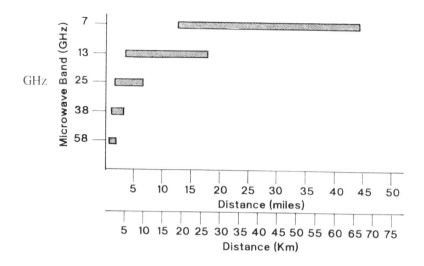

Figure 3.22 Typical link distance plan for different microwave bands

A microwave link is a good example of the outcome of eqns 2.13 and 2.14 discussed in the previous chapter. In particular, Figure 3.22 shows the likely range achievable for the various microwave frequency bands, between 7 and 60 GHz.

The path loss ideally falls off by 6 dB each time the frequency is doubled, but beyond about 15 GHz rain and the atmosphere in general cause additional path loss. This can be made up by using bigger microwave dishes (gain proportional to diameter squared), but dishes above one metre diameter act as a wind brake and a strong mast support is needed. Also, for a microwave path to work well above a favourable C/N margin, the bore-sight to the next mast, i.e. BSC to a BS, must be maintained.

This explains the rationale behind the plan of Figure 3.22. Small, low weight, dishes operating at 38 GHz are clearly popular for PCS systems; for a BSC to MSC link of a 900 MHz system (GSM, TACS, etc.), a microwave link, with larger dishes at 13 GHz may well be used.

3.7.1 Other services of the network

The network, as with other systems, offers fully automatic calling to and from telephones in the fixed network throughout the world, and also provides access to many of the services available on the fixed network, such as information services. In addition, the mobile switching centres support a range of 'vertical' services to complement the basic cellular service, such as:

- Call divert – all incoming calls are diverted to the specified number.

- Busy divert – incoming calls to a busy mobile are diverted to the specified number.

- No answer divert – incoming calls to a non-active (i.e. switched off) mobile, or to an unanswered mobile, are diverted to the specified number.

- Three-party conference calling – a third person can be brought into an existing conversation.

- Call waiting – an incoming call to a busy mobile is indicated by a tone to the subscriber, who can then pick up the second call, placing the first call on hold.

- Call barring – selective call barring can be invoked to prevent, for example, unauthorized international calling.

Other services provided by the network include a messaging service, a voice messaging service which is fully integrated with the cellular network and mobile numbering scheme, and private wire, which allows customers to take advantage of lower call charges by linking their private network directly to a mobile switching centre.

Further reading

Ahlquist, K.G. (1995). 'Mini-Link E – a new link for flexible transmission in cellular networks', *Ericsson Review*, 4, pp 160-8

Beddoes, E.W. and Germer, R.I. (1987). 'Traffic growth in a cellular telephone network', *Journ. I.E.R.E.*, 57, pp 22-26

Beddoes, E.W. (1991). 'UK cellular radio developments', *Elec. & Comms Eng. J.*, Aug, pp 149-158

Boucher, N.J. (1990). *Cellular Radio Handbook*, Quantum Publishing Inc, USA

Cellular mobile telephone system CMS 88, System description available from Ericsson Radio Systems AB, Sweden

Chia, S.T.S. (1995), 'Radio and system design for a dense urban personal communication network', *Elec & Comms Eng. J.*, Aug, pp 178-184

Cellular mobile telephone system CMS 88, System description available from Ericsson Radio Systems AB, Sweden

Chia, S.T.S. (1995), 'Radio and system design for a dense urban personal communication network', *Elec & Comms Eng. J.*, Aug, pp 178-184
Freeman, R.L. (1987). *Radio System Design for Telecommunications*, 1-100 GHz, Wiley Interscience.

Hughes, C.J. and Appleby, M.S. (1985). 'Definition of a cellular mobile radio system', *IEE Proceedings*, 132 Part F, Aug, pp 416 - 424

Mehrotra, A. (1994). *Cellular Radio: Analog and Digital Systems*, Artech House, USA

Lee, W.C.Y. (1989). *Mobile Cellular Communications Systems*, McGraw-Hill, USA

Thrower, K. (1987). 'Mobile radio possibilities', *Journ. I.E.R.E.*, 57, pp 1-11

4 Analog Cellular Radio Signalling

Unlike the fixed public telephone network (PSTN), the cellular radio telephone system has customers who 'roam' over the network. This is not the same concept as with the cordless telephone, for example, where the customer only moves about the same fixed base station or for that matter, private mobile radio (PMR). The 'roaming' attribute means that the customer could be found any-where within the network, which in the case of several systems can extend over national borders.

To provide this facility a very large amount of signalling overhead is required, some of which has already been referred to in the introductory chapter. This chapter describes the signalling procedures in much greater detail, and the procedures are also applicable to second generation systems. The UK *total access communications system* (TACS) will generally be assumed, unless specific reference is made to other systems.

4.1 Channel trunking needs

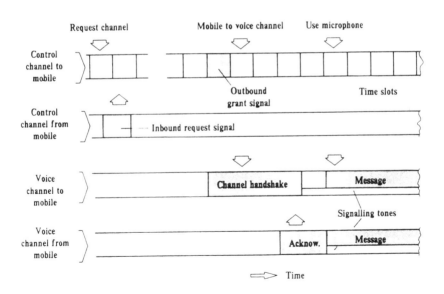

Figure 4.1 Protocol for granting a particular pair of voice channels to a mobile on request

Analog cellular sets up each mobile on a free channel in a cell when the *mobile station* (MS) calls, or is called by the local *base station* (BS). Figure 4.1 shows the strategy for the *control channel* (CC) to allocate a *voice channel* (VC) on request. There is now a tendency to call the voice channels, *traffic channels* (TCH) since they carry the mobile telephony traffic, which could be speech, fax, data, etc.

Continuous carrier transmissions are put in place during the telephone call; in a busy cell all the many transmitters and receivers at the base site could be in operation.

An example protocol between the BS and a single MS is shown in Figure 4.1. The four radio channels are those shown in Figure 1.15, namely the FCC, RCC, FVC and RVC respectively. The *forward* channel pair appear in the BS to MS frequency band; the *reverse* channel pair appear in the MS to BS frequency band, indicated previously in Figure 3.3 and 3.4.

Signalling takes place during the request, handshake and connect periods and clearly constitutes much of the telephone call activity. In cellular, to this signalling must be added the identification, location and handover activities.

In TACS, channels 23-43 and 323-343 are the twenty one per operator *dedicated control channels*, either the FCCs or RCCs, out of the possible one (two) thousand channels in the TACS/GSM spectrum allocation, namely Figure 4.2. These reserved channels are sometimes set aside as optional access channels and optional paging channels.

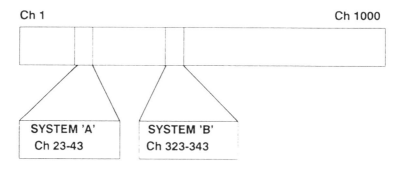

Figure 4.2 The dedicated control channels set aside in the TACS spectrum specification

The data on the *forward voice channel* (FVC) and *reverse voice channel* (RVC) is used for managing the call. Data is transmitted on these channels before, after and during the call. The speech path is muted during the bursts of data, to prevent what would appear as interference to the speech circuit. Speech, data and supervisory tones are transmitted in a frequency shift keying format, each with particular modulation characteristics.

Speech is nominally modulated with a deviation of 5.7 kHz, but is allowed a maximum deviation of 9.5 kHz. This is a wide deviation compared to the channel spacing of 25 kHz and, to ensure that adjacent channels interference is kept to a minimum, adjacent channels are not used in adjoining cells, such as in Figure 3.11.

In comparison, the *supervisory audio tone* (SAT) is deviated by only a small amount, 1.7 kHz, but covers a cluster of cells, as explained earlier in Figure 1.6, and whose purpose is explained again towards the end of this chapter.

All other data is sent at 8 kbps and is modulated onto the carrier using FSK with a deviation of 6.4 kHz. The 8 kHz *signalling tone* (ST) used for hook status alert and call status, is modulated with 6.4 kHz deviation.

Before FSK transmission, the data is Manchester encoded as shown in Figure 4.3. This data *encoding* gives three benefits; namely, strings of ones or zeros can be sent without causing dc offset from entering into the signal level, synchronization is assured, and error detection is practical. However, the actual data rate is only half the signalling rate, i.e. 4 kpbs rather than 8 kbps.

4.2 AMPS/TACS/NAMPS differences

The Region 2 radio frequencies (Figures 1.9) give rise to the North American AMPS system, whereas the UK TACS system tends to be used in the other radio regions. They have close similarity except for details, as can be seen by examining Table 4.1. Therefore, in describing the details of one, one also describes the other.

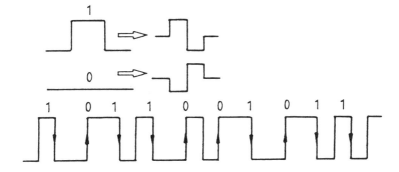

Figure 4.3 Bi-phase signalling known as Manchester encoded data

Table 4.1 Radio interface specification of AMPS, ETACS and NAMPS

Parameter	AMPS	ETACS	NAMPS
Access	FDMA	FDMA	FDMA
Channel Bandwidth	30 kHz	25 kHz	10 kHz
Traffic Channels per RF Channel	1	1	1
Reverse Channel Frequencies*	824-849 MHz	872 -905 MHz	824-849 MHz
Forward Channel Frequencies*	869-894 MHz	917-950 MHz	869-894 MHz
Voice Modulation	FM	FM	FM
Peak Deviation :	±12 kHz	± 9.5 kHz	± 2.5 kHz
Voice Channels	± 8 kHz	± 6.4 kHz	± 8 kHz
Control/Wideband Data			
Channel Coding for	BCH(20,28)	BCH(40,28)	Same as AMPS
Data Transmission	on FCH	on FCH	on CCH; except
	BCH(48,36)	BCH(48,36)	TCHs
	on RCH	on RCH	
Data Rate on Channels	10 kbps	8 kbps	200 bps on TCH
SAT tones	3 @ 6 kHz	3 @ 6 kHz	7 digit DSAT
Number of channels	832	1000	832 × 3 possible

* See Figure 3.3 and 3.4 for full details

4.2.1 NAMPS details

Narrowband AMPS (NAMPS) has also been included in Table 4.1 because it shows how improved systems can be developed (as semiconductor technology progresses), yet maintaining compatibility.

NAMPS takes each 30 kHz AMPS channel and splits it into three 10 kHz channels (Figure 3.1 earlier demonstrated a 2:1 channel improvement strategy). The resulting three-for-one split results in an increase in system capacity without the overhead of cell splitting and all its attendant complexities. NAMPS is compatible with the AMPS system in that the 30 kHz control channel is *still* used and mobile stations can be built to handle both standards. NAMPS has additional features beyond increased capacity which makes it attractive to service providers. These are:

- Dual-mode operation: the NAMPS standard actually specifies operation in both AMPS and NAMPS channels. Thus, an NAMPS compatible mobile station may be directed to an AMPS channel, depending on resources available at the dual-mode cell site. For example, handover from an AMPS channel to an NAMPS channel, or vice versa, is possible using a dual-mode mobile station.

- ARQ signalling: the 200 bps signalling does away with the 10 kHz tones that AMPS uses. It is now possible for the mobile station to acknowledge orders that it has received from the base station. This is especially important in the area of handover where the AMPS handover order confirmation of 50 ms of 10 kHz signalling tone was often missed due to interference.
- Improved call control: the NAMPS specification provides for a feature known as *mobile reported interference* (MRI). The base station can request that the mobile station send in a measure of the forward TCH signal strength, as well as a measure of the number of errors in the 200 bps signalling stream. The base station may then use this information as further input to the handover and power control detection software. This feature arises in the newer digital technologies described in later chapters.
- Likewise, the more recent short message service opportunity can be put in place. Alphanumeric messages of 14 characters or less may be sent on the forward channel in a point-to-point or point-to-multipoint mode, thus combining paging functions with cellular service.
- Preloading: since mobile stations are dual-mode, subscriber equipment to support NAMPS may be offered in advance of NAMPS service actually becoming available.

The key to the 10 kHz channel spectrum usage is the sub-audible signalling scheme employed between the base station and mobile station. A 200 bps continuous data stream is now sent. The user does not hear the signalling, because the frequency resides well below the usable portion of the audio spectrum; Figure 4.4 illustrates this point.

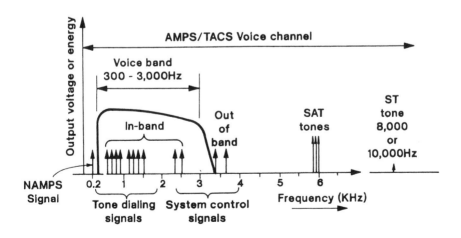

Figure 4.4 The baseband spectrum associated with AMPS, ETACS and NAMPS

Taking the place of the SAT and signalling tone is a sequence of digital words in the 200 bps stream. NAMPS provides for seven digital SAT (DSAT) sequences that have cross-correlation properties chosen to enhance discrimination between the sequences. *Digital signalling tone* (DST) consists of the logical inverses of the seven DSAT sequences. The DSAT and DST are used in place of the SAT and signalling tone, respectively, in the same instances as AMPS, as explained more fully below.

4.2.2 The NMT System

Before doing this it is perhaps helpful to set out corresponding details of the Nordic Mobile System (NMT) which highlights the main differences. (To some extent this explains the motivation for second generation systems and also the concept of dual-mode handsets.)

Table 4.2 Radio interface specification of NMT

Parameter	NMT 450	NMT900
Channel Bandwidth	25(20) kHz	25(12½) kHz
Reverse channel frequencies	453-457 MHz	890-915 MHz
Forward channel frequencies	463-467 MHz	935-960 MHz
Duplex separation	10 MHz	45 MHz
Digital modulation	FFSK	FFSK
Channels	one 'calling'CH	Several 'traffic'CH (some for control and voice)
Data rate	1200 bps including FEC	1200 bps including FEC
SAT tones	4 @ 4 kHz	4 @ 4 kHz
Number of channels (interleaved)	180 (225)	1000 (1999)

An important distinction is that whereas NMT appears to signal more slowly at 1200 bps, FFSK is very robust (see paging below), and also fewer channels have to be reserved exclusively as control channels.

4.3 Equipment identity numbers

On delivery, every mobile is programmed with three numbers, namely,

ESN Electronic Serial No. (32 bits)

MIN Mobile Identity No. (34 bits)

AI   Area Identification (15 bits)

When the mobile is switched on, it reads this data contained in the internal PROM memory of the phone (MS), in particular, the MIN code, as shown here.

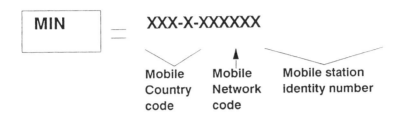

The MIN is a 34-bit binary number derived from a decimal number containing the mobile country code (MCC), the mobile network code (MNC) and a mobile station identity number (MSIN), which were the numbers discussed in section 11 of Chapter 1.

The *electronic serial number* (ESN) is of importance to the network operator, because it is the number which identifies the phone to the network, allows calls to be accepted or received, and also arranges for billing of the call charges to the operator (or owner) of the particular phone. Not long ago, the cloning of stolen equipment, in order to have the same ESN as an authentic paying customer took place, but procedures have now been introduced to curb this illegal activity. For example, scrambling of the ESN as well as changing the encoding from one call to the next now takes place. There is the need for a procedure of *authentication* to take place, which is a particular *forte* of GSM.

The *area identification* code refers to the location area in which the mobile plans to operate, in particular, a specific cell cluster. This is very much related to handover strategies and location changes and is described in detail under the GSM signalling operation.

The MIN number, as already discussed, refers the mobile to the supporting fixed network of the cellular radio system in which the MS is valid to operate. The important components of the fixed network in this respect are the *mobile switching centres* (MSC) and the locations registers, namely a *home location register* (HLR) and *visitors' location register* (VLR).

Thus, when a mobile phone is switched on its data will be retrieved from a home location register (HLR) from somewhere in the network and possibly stored in a visitors location register (VLR) on the switch serving the cells in the area where the phone is located at the time. The HLR will note the identity of the current VLR and the fact that the mobile is active. Incoming calls for the mobile will interrogate the HLR, based on knowledge of the mobile's number and where each number is stored. If the mobile is deemed active, the call will be routed to the appropriate VLR for paging the mobile. This was shown in Figure 3.20 above.

Mobiles will also re-register periodically (typically every 15 minutes) to let the system know that they are still active. If unsuccessful, they will be marked inactive by the system after a period of 5 minutes and thus not paged. This is the process that occurs when a mobile is switched off, or is temporarily unable to register due to loss of signal.

Mobiles also re-register when they cross from one switch area to another, resulting in a cancellation of the first VLR entry and the creation of a second VLR entry on the switch serving the new area. In this way calls can be correctly routed to the mobile as it moves from one location area, or indeed one cell, to another.

Subscribers, in the main, are distributed evenly across switch databases and therefore the network is dimensioned in recognition of the fact that all subscribers are roaming most of the time.

The need to provide national coverage usually results initially in a number of switches being strategically placed across the country of concern at centres of traffic in order to optimize the cost of cell-to-switch transmission links. As traffic increases, additional switch sites are acquired, to accommodate the mobile switching centres, and these switches will be distributed across many sites.

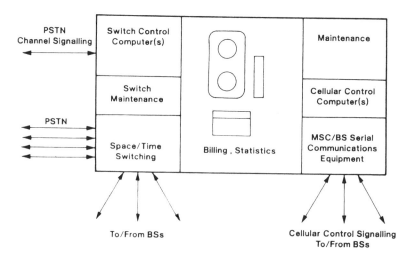

Figure 4.5 The component parts of a mobile switching centre of the analog generation

Again, initially, switches were fully meshed. However, in order to create a manageable network and minimize link costs, as the number of switches has increased, a two-tier approach has been adopted by the creation of an overlay *transit switching centre* (TSC) network, as used in the PSTN. MSCs are connected to at least two TSCs for security, the TSCs being fully meshed. Figure 1.8 of the introductory chapter indicated this arrangement, but left out the full connectivity in the interests of clarity.

A mobile switching network is often considered to be the implementation of an intelligent network. This is because it has to manage the mobility of the subscriber by routing calls to him correctly as his location changes and deal intelligently with mobiles that are out of range.

An outline of an MSC in the analog networks is shown in Figure 4.5. The actual switch, more usually of the PSTN T-S-T design, is only a part of the set up. For example, many common signalling features, maintenance procedures and general network management tasks must be included.

4.4 Radio link signalling details

As mentioned earlier, when a mobile is switched on, it reads its MIN code. It then scans the preferred dedicated control channels. If the dedicated control channel is not set up for combined paging and access, the mobile will be told to tune to a paging channel. The mobile will then remain on this channel in the monitoring mode.

It is perhaps important to recognize the two activities which mark a cellular phone from other radio services. For example, to make a call the MS simply sends a signal on the forward control channel to *request* service. To be called, however, this activity is much more like a *paging* activity. A popular paging protocol is the Post Office Standardization Group (POCSAG) code.

The signal format structure of the POCSAG code is shown in Figure 4.6. This shows that the transmission starts with a preamble followed by batches of code words. Each batch consists of a synchronization code word followed by 8 frames. One frame is equivalent to two code words. Each pager is allocated to one frame of the 8 frames, based on a pre-assigned radio identity code (RIC), which represents the number used by the network to determine the pager for which the call is specified. A pager will switch off if its address is not transmitted in the associated frame. By using this technique, the pager is switched on only for 18% of the transmission time. Battery saving is therefore achieved, besides the saving by omitting the preamble. This is a feature of interest to cellular radio handsets.

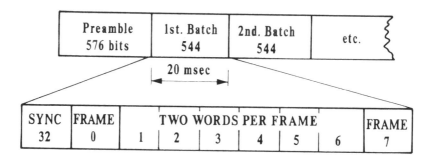

Figure 4.6 Structure of POCSAG code

The code is based on a (31,21) BCH code. An even parity bit is added to form a 32 bit code word. The code supports tone, numeric and alphanumeric paging services, and usually runs at a 1200 bps data rate.

The paging signal just outlined runs more or less continuously (depending on paging traffic); in cellular the paging transmission is kept on continuously as a 'beacon' marker.

It is helpful to recall Figure 1.14 again, because of the channel nomenclature specific to TACS (and AMPS) cellular, namely the forward and reverse channel designations.

The information sent by a base station on the forward path of the dedicated control channel (FCC) is now described in detail.

4.4.1 *Forward control channel messages*

Each frame of the data stream contains bit sync and word sync for mobiles to obtain synchronization. *Busy/idle* bits are sent at the beginning of every bit sync sequence, word sync sequence, first repeat of word A and every ten message bits thereafter to indicate the state of the reverse channel. The information is sent in 40-bit words and can take the form of one of three types of message:

Overhead messages
Mobile station control messages
Control filler messages

Unlike the other control and the two voice channels, the forward control channel consists of a *continuously* transmitted data stream; in addition, every word is repeated five times to give adequate error protection against fading.

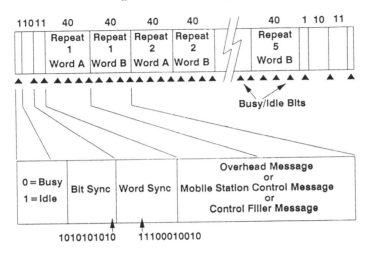

Figure 4.7 Content outline of the FCC signal

4.4.2 Overhead messages

These contain general data on the local system for all mobiles to receive.

Overhead messages provide the mobiles with information on the local system, such as the area identification (AI) and what access and paging channels are available in that particular cell.

The first two bits (T1, T2) will always be set to '11' to signify an overhead message.

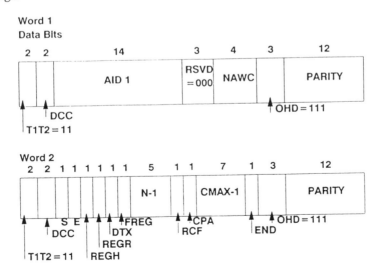

Figure 4.8 Details of the overhead messages within each FCC word

The interpretation of the data field is as follows:

TI T2 Type field. Set to '11', indicates an overhead word.

DCC Digital colour code field; see Figure 1.5.

AID 1 First part of the traffic area identification field.

RSVD Reserved for future use, all bits set as indicated.

NAWC Number of additional words coming field. In word 1 this field is set to one fewer than the total number of words in the overhead message train.

OHD Overhead message type field. The OHD field of word 1 is set to '110' indicating the first word of the system parameter overhead message. The OHD field of word 2 is set to '111' indicating the second word of the system parameter overhead message.

P Parity field.

S Serial number field.

E Extended address field.

REGH Registration field for mobile stations operating on their preferred system.

REGR Registration field for mobile stations not operating on their preferred system.

DTX Discontinuous transmission field.

FREG Forced registration field.

N The number of paging channels in the system.

RCF Read control filler field.

CPA Combined paging/access field.

CMAX This is the number of access channels in the system.

END End indication field. Set to '1' to indicate the last word of the overhead message train; set to '0' if not last word.

The control channel in AMPS uses the 10 kHz FSK signalling to communicate with mobile stations in a point-to-point or point-to-multipoint mode. The forward control channel carries *busy-idle status* (BIS) signal to all mobile stations. This bit informs all mobile stations as to the status of the reverse control channel. Since the reverse control channel is multiple access (multipoint-to-point), the BIS signals whether or not a mobile station is currently using the reverse control channel to communicate with the system. This mechanism reduces the probability of collision on the reverse control channel due to several mobile stations trying to access the system at the same time.

Discontinuous transmission (DTX) is the term used to describe an operating mode in which the mobile station gates its transmitter output power as a function of speech activity on the part of the user. DTX may not be used by a mobile station unless it is allowed in the system. Two bits in the overhead message of the control channel indicate the DTX permissions in the system. When a mobile station is in the *DTX-high* state and is involved in a call with a cell site, it radiates at either the maximum amount of power it is capable of, the maximum amount of power for which it is allowed in that particular cell site, or the most recently commanded power. When it is in the *DTX-low* state, the mobile station radiates at a level 8 dB below the DTX-high state or at any level up to the DTX-high state. The choice of DTX-low transmission power mode is up to the service provider. The reduction in radiated power (about 16% of the DTX-high state in the 8 dB reduction case) allows a battery savings in proportion to the voice activity.

4.4.3 Mobile station control messages on FCC

These are specific to a particular mobile, and contain the following messages:

```
Page mobile     = MIN
Power level     = VMAC
Voice channel   = CHAN
SAT frequency   = SCC
```

Mobile station control messages are sent to tell individual mobiles what is required of them. Messages for even-numbered mobiles are sent in word A, odd numbers in word B, shown in the FCC message sequence, Figure 4.7.

The message may be up to four words long and will have the first two bits (T1, T2) set to '00' if a single word is sent, otherwise multiple word messages will have word 1 set to '01', with remaining words set to '10'.

The message will always contain the mobile identity number (MIN). Depending on the action required, there may also be the *mobile attenuation code* (VMAC), the SAT *colour code* (SCC) and the *voice channel* (CHAN) assigned.

4.4.4 Control filler messages

Control filler messages are data words sent to ensure the continuous stream of data on the forward control channel; in other words they can be monitored as a continuous carrier, and contain certain additional data fields indicating whether the overhead message must be read before attempting a system access.

These messages also contain power level information for the mobile on the reverse control channel and the digital colour code.

4.5 Registration

Registration is used by mobiles to announce their current location and enable the network to direct incoming calls to the appropriate cells. Mobiles are forced to register when crossing from one traffic area to another, or on command from a base station on a periodic basis, as depicted in Figure 3.18.

The mobile will have powered up, stored information from a dedicated control channel and then go into the monitoring mode, where it listens to control channel messages.

If it is necessary to perform a registration the mobile must first access the system. This means monitoring the busy/idle bits on the forward control channel and attempting to seize the channel when it is idle. On seizing the channel, it sends a burst of identification data on the reverse control channel.

4.5.1 Reverse control channel messages

The reverse control channel (RCC) is used by the mobile to send information to the network. It is sent as a burst of data and, like the FCC, each word is repeated five times, as shown in Figure 4.9.

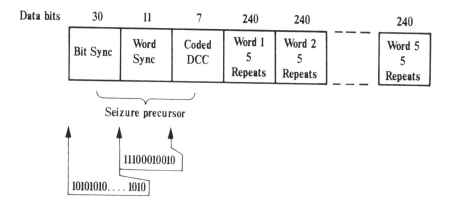

Figure 4.9 Outline of RCC signalling format

Bit sync and a coded DCC are sent before the information words. The two-bit DCC is derived from a seven-bit DCC sent by the base station to ensure that the correct base station has been seized.

If the mobile is only performing a registration it will send three words containing the mobile identity number (MIN), electronic serial number (ESN) and other data such as *station class mark* (SCM) of mobile.

4.6 Mobile call initiation

- The mobile user starts the process by selecting a number to be called; this is normally done by loading a number via the key pad. When the *send* key (off-hook) is pressed the mobile checks the system access data, monitors the busy/idle bits, and performs a system access.

- The mobile sends data over the RCC containing the mobile MIN number, the ESN and the called number. The process is now close to the scheme shown in Figure 4.1.

- The system changes the busy/idle bits to busy and processes the received mobile data, checking that it is valid on the system.

- The system sends a mobile control message to allocate a voice channel for the conversation and at the same time sets up the call on the voice channel, sending the relevant SAT tone.

- The mobile checks the data and stores it in memory, then moves to the voice channel where it transponds the SAT frequency (one of three) to confirm that the channel is set up.

- A conversation path is now open and the mobile user will hear a ringing tone until the call is answered.

4.7 Mobile call reception

- On receipt of an incoming call the system generates a mobile station control message over the FCC to page the mobile.

- The mobile monitors the busy/idle bits, and when the control channel is free, performs a system access by sending data over the RCC containing its MIN, ESN and a paging order confirmation message.

power levels, perform handovers and send additional service request information.

The forward voice channel message contains single 40-bit words, repeated 11 times between syncs and word syncs.

The reverse voice channel can contain up to five words consisting of either, order confirmation for the base station, or a called address for an additional service request.

All messages contain bits to determine the number of additional words, type of word and parity.

In summary, the data format on the four channels connecting each BS and MS, are as follows:

	Bits per word	*No of repeats*	*No of words*
FCC	40	5	Continuous
RCC	48	5	3-7*
FVC	40	11	1
RVC	48	5	1-5

* to allow for dialled digits

4.7.1 The signalling tone

In addition to the data, the two supervisory audio tones, used for additional control via the voice channels, are very important. They have been spoken about, but bear more explanation.

ST is a tone of 8 kHz ±1 kHz, modulated at a nominal deviation of 6.4 kHz and is used for four activities:

- *Confirmation of handover request:* on receipt of a command to 'handover' the mobile stores the new channel number, SAT, and power level, and sends the ST for 50 ms before handing over.

- *Hookflash:* during conversation for additional services. The user loads the type of service via his keypad and presses the 'send' key. A 400 ms burst of ST is sent over the RVC to request a hookflash.

- *Cleardown:* on termination of a call by the mobile user, i.e. press on-hook, the ST is sent for 1.8 seconds over the RVC.

- *Confirmation of alert:* after a mobile is alerted, the ST is sent via the RVC for several seconds until the call is answered by the mobile user.

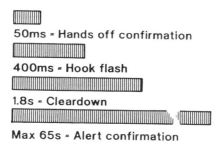

50ms - Hands off confirmation

400ms - Hook flash

1.8s - Cleardown

Max 65s - Alert confirmation

Figure 4.11 The four duration times of the signalling tone on AMPS/TACS

4.7.2 *The supervisory audio tone*

The second tone is the supervisory audio tone (SAT). These (three) tones are again a critical part of analog cellular and have two functions.

As described in Chapter 1, section 9, it enables base stations in one particular cluster to be distinguished from base stations in a neighbouring cluster using the same channel frequencies. The MS is therefore constrained to operate to the base station in its vicinity even though it could be receiving an adjacent cluster channel frequency, but with the incorrect SAT.

The second use of the SAT is to maintain a closed identification loop for the base station. If SAT is lost during a call the mobile unit starts a timer; if the SAT is not received before the timer expires, the call is terminated. The mobile is advised which SAT to expect at initial call set up by the SAT colour code (SCC) on the FVC, shown in the table below.

The frequency of the generated SAT should be accurate to 1 Hz.

SAT Frequency (Hz)	SCC
5970	00
6000	01
6030	10

4.7.3 *Handover*

- If during conversation the received signal strength falls low, as determined by a SINAD measurement at the BS receiver, and the mobile is on the maximum power level for the particular cell, the base station sends a message to the mobile switching centre.

- The system, by means of the BS-MSC hierarchy, initiates a search for a better cell by requesting adjacent cells to measure the signal strength of the relevant mobile, by means of a monitoring receiver.

- If a stronger signal is found, and a free channel on a (new) frequency is available in that cell, a second voice path is set up through that cell and bridged across to the existing one in preparation for a handover.

- The system generates a handover order over the initial forward voice channel.

- The mobile stores the handover data which includes the new channel number, SAT and power level; it then sends a signalling tone ST for 50 ms and turns off the initial reverse voice channel.

- The mobile re-tunes to the new voice channel, turns its transmitter on, and the new SAT is transponded.

- When the system detects the SAT, the former base station channel is released for possible other activity.

4.8 Illustration of signalling procedures

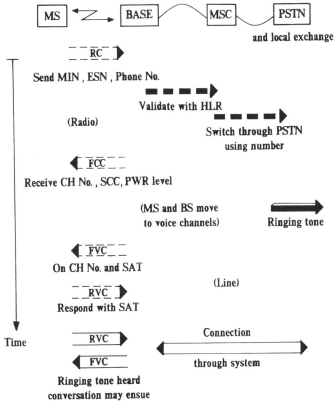

Figure 4.12 Mobile-originating call. (Data = dashed lines; voice signals = continuous.)

It is helpful to visualize the signalling procedure of cellular as calls are set up by means of a 'moving' diagram.

Figure 4.12 shows the procedure which takes place for making a call from the mobile subscriber to a subscriber in the fixed network (or it could be another mobile located in the network).

The local MSC may contain the HLR, but certainly a VLR. The data transmission process on TACS requires a minimum of 2620 bits (because of the intensive repetition) which takes 327 msec at an 8 kbps signalling rate. In AMPS the signalling pattern is similar, except that it occurs at 10 kbps (in a 30 kHz BW). In NMT the signalling rate is only 1200 bps, but only requires 64 signalling bits.

The action for a fixed network subscriber calling a mobile is shown in Figure 4.13.

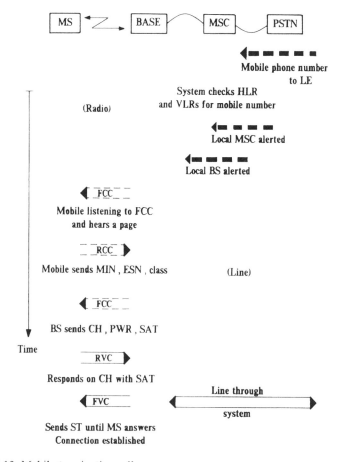

Figure 4.13 Mobile-terminating call

In the case of handover, data signalling occurs only over the forward and reverse voice channels. These are above the voice (audio) band (except in the case of NAMPS) and the user is unaware of the signalling, except for a short muting action, usually of less than 300 msec duration. The action is shown in Figure 4.14.

It is worth noting that extensive signalling takes place in cellular radio, chiefly because of the roaming characteristics of the mobile subscribers. However, a very large proportion of the data bits used are for signal security, either by extensive code correction or multiple repetition. This is due to the unavoidable multipath propagation condition in UHF radio circuits. We explore multipath propagation and its effect on signalling in Chapter 5.

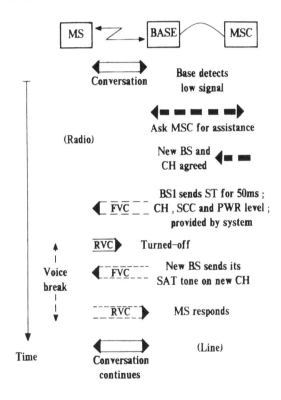

Figure 4.14 Handover activity

4.9 Data over cellular

The interesting fact about signalling within an analog cellular radio network is that much of the messaging is digital. There is therefore good reason to suppose that data messaging services can be set up on an analog cellular system – and even more reason to suppose data services can be expected within a digital cellular network. However, there are some data specific services which make definite use of the cellular radio principle. By these one does not mean data-over-voice services with mobile terminals, or even facsimile. Such services use the voice channels in analog cellular, as set up by the digital signalling protocol just described. There are of course several difficulties with this approach, due to marginal error rates on a cellular voice path, and ARQ as well as FEC for error correction are used. The methods and systems are beyond the scope of this text, however.

4.9.1 Data specific networks

It is of interest on the other hand to describe one specific network because it illustrates how a different system, or perhaps service, can come about due to the differences between cellular systems, rather than principle, as set out in Chapter 1, section 12. Such a particular system is known as PAKNET and provides a packet data network, by means of transparent VHF cellular radio operation.

The basic elements of the scheme are shown in Figure 4.15. A similar set is distributed over a seven-cell cluster like Figure 3.11; the main difference being that the cell radii are generally larger because lower VHF frequencies are licensed for the service. The precise frequencies are indicated in Table 4.3.

Fourteen channels are allocated to the base stations which contain the *network access controller* (NAC); fourteen lower frequencies are allocated to the receiving stations containing a *network terminating unit* (NTU). Only seven pairs with 25 kHz channel spacing are used; the extra pairs are for standby or possible system expansion. Note that the T_x/R_x spacing is now only 4.5 MHz, unlike the 45 MHz of conventional cellular. Also note that the service range can be some three times greater compared to conventional cellular, a point illustrated by Figure 2.11.

Because PAKNET is a data specific network, the control channel(s) in each cell acts as both control and signalling. Thus, whereas cellular signals over the forward and reverse control channels, it has to switch to voice channels for messaging, as shown in Figure 4.1. In PAKNET only two channels are involved, and signalling in the time slots is shown in Figure 4.16. The signalling rate used is 8 kbps, using direct frequency modulation of each RF carrier. The protocol used is a random multiple access protocol, known as dynamic slotted reservation, or ALOHA. Thus, whereas the access periods in Figure 4.16 are marked by the base station, the request-to-transmit a data packet by an NTU, is random among a set of users in a particular cell. This is what leads to the maximum number of users that one particular cell can support, because of possible collision in the request-to-transmit period R. However, the system has been dimensioned so that up to 800 terminals, operating at an average rate of one transaction (packet) every 15 minutes, can be supported in each cell.

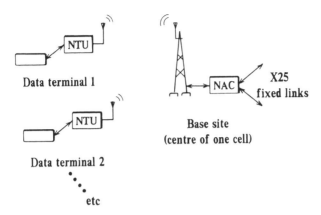

Figure 4.15 The principal components within the PAKNET data specific network

Table 4.3 The frequencies allocated to PAKNET

Channel	BS transmit	BS receive	
1	164.2125 MHz	159.7125 MHz)	(Guard channel
2	164.225	159.725	
3	164.2375	159.7375	
4	164.245	159.75	
- - -	- - -	- - - -	
13	164.3625	159.8625	
14	164.375	159.875	
15	164.3875	159.8875	
16	164.4	159.9	(Guard channel)

To protect the user data, typically 128 bytes, a 12:12 FEC protocol is used, backed up by a 16-bit *cyclic redundancy check* (CRC) to detect any remaining errors. Since the system in principle is used for monetary transaction data services, no transmission errors can be accepted. Hence if the CRC identifies any errors, an ARQ operation, as discussed in section 1.10, is put into operation, that is, via transmission block A in Figure 4.16. Apart from these details, the closeness of the system to the signalling part of analog cellular is very evident.

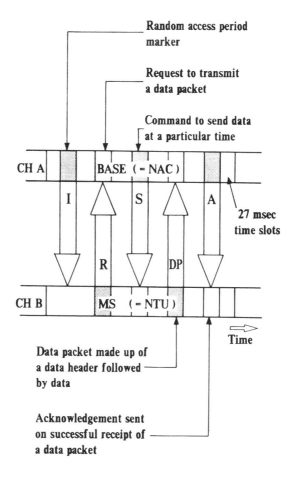

Figure 4.16   Signalling (packet) activity in the forward and return channels of the
               PAKNET system

Further reading

Beddoes, E.W. and Eastead, J.R. (1993).'TACS: the UK approach' in *Cellular
Radio Systems*, Artech House, N.J.

Davie, M.C. and Smith, J.B. (1991). 'A cellular packet radio data network',
Elec & Comms J, June, pp 137-143

Flack, M. and Gronow, M. (1990). *Cellular Communication for Data Transmission*, NCC Blackwell, UK

Hughes, C.J. and Appleby, M.S. (1985). 'Definition of a cellular mobile radio system, *Proc IEE*, 132 Part F, August, pp 416-424

Lee, W.C.Y. (1989). *Mobile Cellular Communication Systems*, McGraw-Hill, USA, Ch 3.

Menich, B.J. (1993). 'Analog Cellular Radio in the United States' in *Cellular Radio Systems*, Artech House, N.J.

Parsons, J.D. and Gardiner, J.G. (1989). *Mobile Communication Systems*, Blackie, UK

Philips Telecommunication Review (1983). 'Special issue on mobile radio', April

5 The Multipath Propagation Problem

5.1 General considerations

The properties and principles outlined so far in respect of cellular radio would appear to show that a roaming radiotelephone system can be set up quite specifically. Radio coverage in a cell can be well defined; co-channel interference from adjacent cells can likewise be defined; analog voice with FM operates in an assured manner; signalling over the network can be defined accurately, which likewise sets the pattern for digital cellular systems to be described in the following chapters. Are there remaining problems, and why is there the desire to move to digital cellular radio?

There are two main problems:

(i)   The radio signals are much less well defined than we have so far indicated. Scattering and reflection, plus movement of the user, causes what is known as *multipath propagation*. This effect causes errors in the signalling – hence the large amount of redundancy in the signalling patterns – and also puts limits on the co-channel operation in closely packed cells, especially when consisting of multiple continuous wave FM systems

The cell packing determines the efficiency of the cellular scheme and in turn the number of users. Digital cellular technology can offer improved efficiency of the limited available radio spectrum, a subject discussed in some detail towards the end of the book.

(ii) The fixed telephone network is nearly all digital; all voice messages are encoded and transmitted in a PCM format. The same arrangement is the aim of the mobile phone network operators. All messages and signalling would be digital.

Because the bandwidth available in the mobile (radio) part of the network is severely limited, however, more speed-efficient coding algorithms are necessary. Also, the digital signalling rate per Hertz should be high. Digital cellular has addressed both these problems, again under the shadow of multipath propagation.

It is also important to note another advantage that can arise by switching to digital operation, namely 'universality'. The network can be more readily extended across national borders, allowing international roaming of subscribers. This concept is described in Chapter 9.

5.2 Multipath fading characteristics

The multipath problem in mobile radio is caused by reflection and scattering from buildings, hills and other obstacles along the radio path. Radio waves arrive at a mobile receiver from many different directions, with different time delays. If one refers back to Figure 2.6, an extra ray path was shown coming from a scattering source (a building). Together with a possible direct ray, a ground reflected ray and other possible scattered rays, these combine vectorially at the receiver antenna to give a resultant signal which depends on the differences in path length that exist in this multipath field. Also, as a vehicle-borne, or handheld, receiver moves from one location to another, the phase relationship between the components of the various incoming waves changes so the resultant signal changes. It is important to note that whenever relative motion exists there is a Doppler shift of the frequency components within the received signal.

Characterising the mobile radio channel is therefore not a simple task. It is possible, however, to deal with the problem in two ways. Firstly, we can consider the case where the signals occupy only a narrow bandwidth. By 'narrowband' we mean that the spread of *time delays* in the multipath environment is sufficiently small for all spectral components within the transmitted message to be affected in a similar way. By time delays we refer to the time of travel, at the speed of light, from the transmitter (BS, say) to the mobile, and these will clearly vary according to the diversity of the path. Previously, we had referred to these difference as phase differences. At a frequency f, over a path length difference of 2π, or one wavelength, the excess path delay is clearly $1/f$, see Figure 2.1. At 900 MHz this time delay difference would be 1.1 nanoseconds.

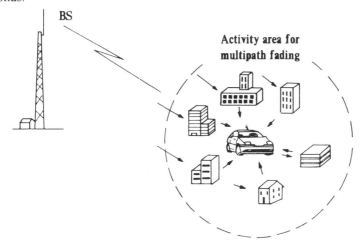

Figure 5.1 Illustration of radio propagation in an urban area

In the narrowband case there are only minor frequency-selective effects and the characteristics of the channel can be expressed in terms of their effect on any one component in the message – the carrier frequency is usually used. A more complicated form of characterization is needed to deal with wideband signals; 'wideband' in this case is used to indicate that frequency-selective effects do occur.

First we deal with the narrowband case in order to introduce ideas and terminology relevant to this subject. In urban areas problems exist due to the fact that the mobile antenna is low, so there is generally no line-of-sight path to the base station which itself is often located in close proximity to buildings. Propagation is therefore mainly by means of scattering and multiple reflections from the surrounding obstacles, as shown in Figure 5.1. Because the wavelengths in UHF bands are less than 1 metre, the position of the antenna does not have to be changed very much to change the signal level by several tens of dB.

This feature is known as slow fading and is observed as the position of the mobile is changed. It can be experienced in FM car radios and VHF private mobile radio (PMR) equipment. The signal appears to vanish at certain positions, but moving only a few metres brings it back again. The signal envelope takes on a standing wave pattern, as shown in Figure 5.2, and is characterized by a log-normal probability density function. The mean signal level, about 3 dB below any peak value, is the one calculated in Chapter 2.

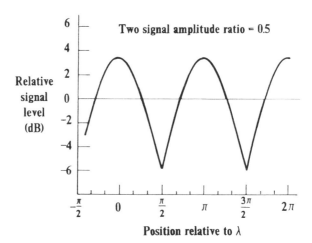

Figure 5.2 Standing wave pattern due to two carrier waves being received at the same time versus their relative phase

A receiver moving continuously through this field experiences a time-related variable signal which is further complicated by the existence of Doppler shift.

The signal fluctuations caused by the local multipath are now known as *fast fading,* to distinguish them from the much more leisurely variation in mean level, referred to above as slow fading. A record of fast fading is shown in Figure 5.3. Fades of a depth less than 20 dB occur quite often, but deeper fades in excess of 30 dB are fortunately less frequent. Rapid fading is usually observed over distances of about half a wavelength; therefore, at VHF and UHF, a vehicle moving at 50 km/hr or 19 m/sec, will pass through several fades in a second.

Examination of Figure 5.3 shows that it is possible to draw a distinction between the short-term multipath effects and the longer-term variations of the local mean. Here, however, we consider only the short-term effects both for narrowband and wideband channels; in other words, we consider signal statistics in which the mean level of the signal is constant.

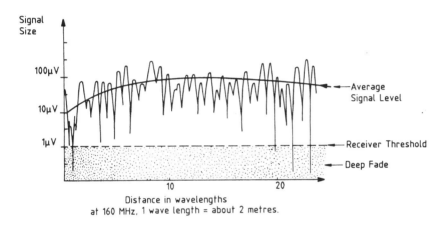

Figure 5.3 Illustration of typical envelope pattern of a VHF signal received under multipath conditions

5.2.1 *Elementary multipath*

A multipath propagation situation always contains several different paths by which energy travels from the transmitter to the receiver. If we consider the case of a stationary receiver, one can imagine a static multipath situation in which several versions of the signal arrive sequentially at the receiver. The effect of the differential time delays is to introduce relative phase shifts between the component waves and superposition of the different components leads to either constructive or destructive addition, depending upon the relative phases. Figure 5.4 illustrates the resultant signal arising from two paths.

When either the transmitter or the receiver is in motion, we have a dynamic multipath situation in which there is a continuous change in the electrical length of every propagation path and thus the relative phase shifts between them change as a function of spatial location.

The time variations, or dynamic changes in the propagation path lengths, can be related directly to the motion of the receiver and indirectly to the Doppler effects that arise. In a practical case, the several incoming paths will be such that their individual phases, as experienced by a moving receiver, will change continuously and randomly.

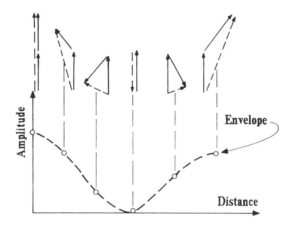

Figure 5.4 Illustrating how the envelope fades as two signals combine with different phases

An established multipath model assumes that the field incident on the mobile antenna is composed of a number of plane waves of random phase, these plane waves being vertically polarized with nearly horizontal angles of arrival and phase angles which are random and statistically independent. Further, the phase angles are assumed to have a uniform probability density function in the interval $(0,2\pi)$. This is reasonable at VHF and above, where the wavelength is sufficiently short to ensure that small changes in path length result in significant changes in the RF phase.

5.2.2 A scattering model

Continuing with this model, therefore, at every receiving point, we assume the existence of n plane waves of similar amplitude. This is a realistic assumption in heavily built-up areas, for example, since the scattered components are likely to experience similar attenuation and there will be no dominant component. In certain situations, a direct line-of-sight path may contribute a steady nonrandom component, but here we restrict our discussion to the case of n equal-amplitude waves.

The path-angle geometry for the scattered plane waves is shown in Figure 5.5.

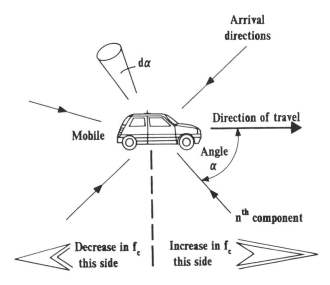

Figure 5.5 Path arrival geometry at a mobile station in a multipath situation. Vehicle motion is indicated

If the transmitted signal is vertically polarized, we assume that the components at the mobile have a vertical electric field E_z. Also, the assumption that the mobile received signal is of the scattered type, with each component wave being independent, randomly phased and having a random angle of arrival, leads to the result that the *probability density function* of the *envelope* R (the vector sum of the quadrature X and Y components) is

$$p_r(R) = \frac{R}{\sigma^2} \exp(-R^2/2\sigma^2)p \tag{5.1}$$

This is called a Rayleigh distribution. The corresponding *cumulative distribution function* P_r is

$$P_r(R) = 1 - \exp(-R^2/2\sigma^2) \tag{5.2}$$

where σ^2 is the mean power. These two functions are shown in Figure 5.6.

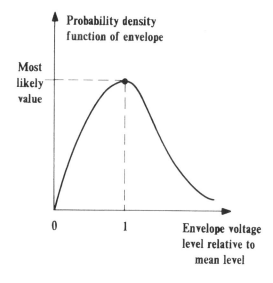

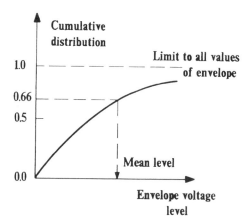

Figure 5.6 The Rayleigh probability density and cumulative distributions functions

Since one is considering the *envelope* of the fading signal, both distributions are always positive functions.

A useful way of understanding the multipath signal, and why it is called Rayleigh fading, is to note a method of simulating such a signal. Thus, as shown in Figure 5.7, an RF signal is divided into two paths; an in-phase path X, and an out-of-phase path Y. Each signal is then modulated by a Gaussian amplitude voltage function which gives to the two components (X and Y) the required signal (±) amplitude variance. Adding the two components produces a signal with the Rayleigh envelope fading function p(R).

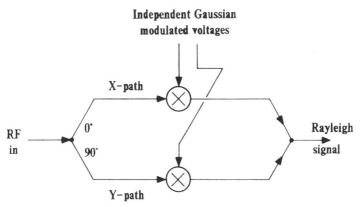

Figure 5.7 Two-path modulation approach to Rayleigh fading signal generation

5.2.3 Effect of vehicle velocity

If either the transmitter or receiver is in motion, the components of the received signal each experience a Doppler shift, the frequency shift being related to the angle between the direction of arrival of that component and the direction of vehicle motion. For a vehicle moving at a constant speed v along the X-axis, as in Figure 5.5, the Doppler shift f_n of the plane-wave component arriving at an angle α_n, is

$$f_n = \frac{v}{\lambda} \cos \alpha_n \tag{5.3}$$

It can be seen that component waves arriving from ahead of the vehicle experience a positive Doppler shift (maximum value $f_d = v/\lambda$), while those arriving from behind the vehicle have a negative shift.

It is worth noting that a speed of 40 mph at 900 MHz, produces a maximum Doppler shift of 53 Hz, i.e.

$$f_d = \frac{v(\text{metres per second})}{\lambda(\text{metres})}$$

$$= \frac{40 \times 8/5 \times 1000}{0.33 \times 60 \times 60} = 53 \text{ Hz}$$

using the conversion of 8 km to every 5 miles, etc. Also, a proportional change in frequency, or speed, will produce a proportional change in f_d.

Thus at a DCS frequency of 1800 MHz, for example, the maximum Doppler shift would increase in this example to 108 Hz. Fortunately, most PCS/DCS systems tend to be used by pedestrians, and therefore the Doppler effect is that much smaller.

If the number of components n is large, the fraction of the incident power contained within angles between α and $\alpha + d\alpha$, for an omnidirectional antenna, is $p(\alpha)d\alpha$. Equating this to the incremental power determined through the relation between the Doppler shift and the nominal carrier frequency f_c, namely,

$$f(\alpha) = f_d \cos \alpha + f_c$$

we can obtain the power spectral density S(f) of the received signal, observed by a vertical antenna, namely

$$S_{EZ}(f) = \frac{1.5}{\pi f_d} \left[\frac{1 - (f - f_c)^2}{f_d} \right]^{0.5} \tag{5.4}$$

This power spectral density function is shown in Figure 5.8.

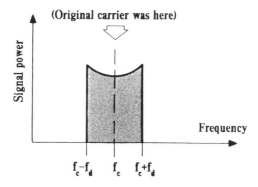

Figure 5.8 Power spectral density function of an RF carrier caused by Rayleigh multipath

If a dominant component exists in the incoming signal, then this has a substantial influence on the signal spectrum. For example, such a component arriving at an angle α_o gives rise to a spectral line at $f_c + f_d \cos \alpha_o$ in the RF spectrum.

In the time domain, the effects of the randomly phased and Doppler-shifted multipath signals appear in the form of a fading envelope, as described previously.

5.2.4 *Fading envelope statistics*

The fading envelope directly affects the performance of any receiver. The Rayleigh fading envelope only occasionally experiences very deep fades, for example 30 dB fades occur for only 0.1% of the time. This can be understood from the signal envelope cumulative probability distribution, shown in Figure 5.9. To specify some of the constraints in a quantitative manner, one parameter in particular that interests us, is how often the envelope crosses a specified signal level.

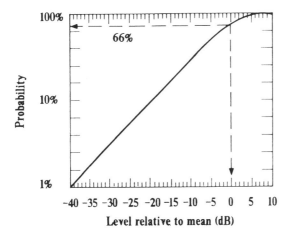

Figure 5.9 Cumulative probability distributions of the signal envelope RMS level

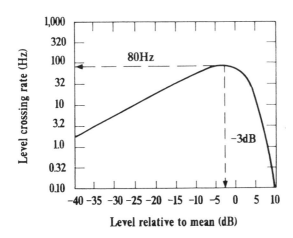

Figure 5.10   The level crossing rate of a fast fading signal envelope versus level relative to RMS value for a 80 Hz Doppler shift

The level crossing rate L at a specified signal level R is defined as the average number of times per second that the signal envelope crosses the level in a positive-going direction.

Figure 5.10 shows a calculated result of this function. The level crossing rate L is shown in Hertz, but is really relative to the maximum Doppler shift frequency f_d. Figure 5.10 assumes that $f_d = 80$ Hz. The levels at which crossings occur are indicated as decibels relative to the RMS signal level. We note that at $L = f_d$ the level is 3 dB below the peak envelope level. Deep fades are much less likely to occur, as was indicated in Figure 5.3.

5.3 Diversity reception

In mobile radio systems, especially at UHF, the effects of fading can be reduced by the use of space diversity techniques, either at the base station or the mobile, provided that two antennas can be separated far enough to ensure that the signal envelopes exhibit a low correlation. The principle of diversity is based on the observation that the envelope covariance function of the component E_z of the signal at the mobile in Figure 5.5, and the same signal at a position removed by a spatial distance d_x/λ, in the case of isotropic scattering, obeys a function which is the square of the first order Bessel function (as in analog FM theory). This function is of course always positive and less than or equal to one.

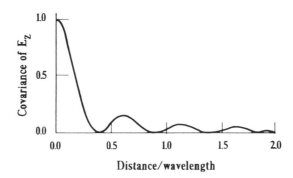

Figure 5.11 Covariance function for the envelope of the electric field

The result is plotted in Figure 5.11 for the case of an isotropically scattered field. There is rapid decorrelation, showing that space diversity could be implemented at the mobile end of the link where the assumption of isotropic scattering is approximately true.

On the other hand, it is less clear that at base station sites the assumption of isotropic scattering will hold. Base station sites are in general chosen to be well above local obstructions in order to give the best coverage of the intended service area, whereas the scattering objects, which produce the multipath effects, are located principally in a small area surrounding the mobile, see Figure 5.1. The reciprocity theorem applies, of course, in a linear medium, but this should not be taken to imply that the spatial correlation distance at one end of the radio path is the same as it is at the other.

It is clear that antennas have to be further apart at base station sites than at mobiles to obtain decorrelation, and indeed this is the case. It is also apparent that whereas at mobiles the assumption of isotropic scattering, from scatterers which surround the mobile uniformly, leads directly to the conclusion that the correlation between the electric field at two receiving points is a function of their separation only, this is not the case at base station sites. Here, scattering is not isotropic and the correlation between the electric field at two receiving points is a function of both their separation and the angle between the line joining them and the direction to the mobile. Nevertheless, antenna diversity is in general use at BS sites for digital systems. The horizontal separation used is usually in the range 10-20 λ. Vertical separation diversity is also possible, but now requires distances of 20-60 λ. The diversity gain achieved is about 4 dB. This does not seem too significant, but if one views Figure 5.2 for example, the chances of a destructive fade on the digital signalling message is much reduced.

5.4 Frequency selective fading

The previous discussion described the envelope and phase variations of the signal received at a moving vehicle when an unmodulated carrier is radiated by the base station transmitter. The question now arises as to whether this description of the channel applies when signals, which occupy a finite bandwidth, are radiated. It is clear that we need to consider the effects of multipath propagation in the case of two or more frequency components within the message bandwidth. If these frequencies are close to each other, then the different propagation paths within the multipath field have approximately the same electrical length for both components, and their amplitude and phase variations will be very similar. This is the narrowband case. As the frequency separation increases, however, the behaviour at one frequency tends to become uncorrelated with that at the other frequency, because the differential phase shifts along the various paths are quite different at the two frequencies.

An example of frequency selective fading is shown in Figure 5.12. One frequency could well suffer a severe fade, whereas the second frequency's fade is delayed in position. This illustrates the potential for diversity by frequency hopping during messaging, a technique employed in digital cellular systems.

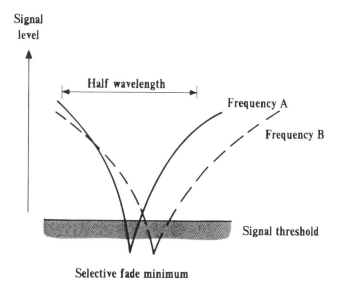

Figure 5.12   Nulls in reception due to two-path interference because of selective fading.
Note how the null of frequency B does not coincide with frequency A

5.4.1 The use of interleaving

Frequency diversity is not always practical, especially on DAMPS/GSM
networks. There is a shortage of channels in busy networks. Frequency hopping
does imply one has a spare frequency to hop to, or indeed a very sophisticated
frequency hopping algorithm for all users, which then really becomes a sort of
CDMA situation (see Chapter 8).

The effect of a deep short fade on a data signal is shown in Figure 5.13.
Provided that the fade does not last too long, then the process of interleaving
(see Figure 1.24) is very effective.

An interesting question is to how long does a deep fade last (in millisecs,
say). This time will quite clearly depend on the speed of travel of the MS.
Figure 5.10 gives the level crossing rate versus signal level where the rate is 80
Hz (a period of 12.5 ms) for 50 mph and using GSM. Quite clearly for the
destructive fades illustrated in Figure 5.13, the duration will surely be less, say
by 1/10th, = 1.25 ms. Although the more serious fade happens far less often,
e.g., Figure 5.10, its duration will remain more or less the same. 1.25 ms
represents about one quarter of a GSM frame period (see chapter 9) and can
clearly take out several time slots. This is why interleaving (Figure 1.24) is so
important. For D-AMPS (Chapter 10), the frame period is very much longer, as
well as the time slots themselves, so this type of deep fade is less destructive.

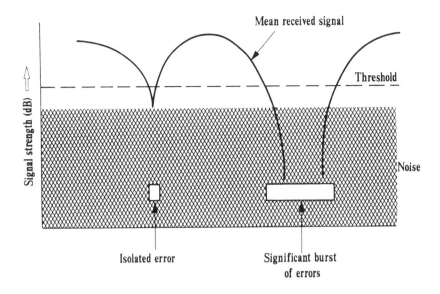

Figure 5.13 Illustrative effect of fading and temporary shadowing on a signal

However, what if the MS moves more slowly, e.g. a pedestrian using a handheld? The Doppler shift frequency now drops to a few Hz, and the corresponding fade duration period will likewise increase. This fade, due to multipath, not shadowing, is quite serious and recommends a frequency hopping strategy, where possible.

5.5 Coherence bandwidth and delay spread

The extent of the decorrelation depends on the spread of time delays, because the phase shifts arise from the excess path lengths. For large delay spreads the phases of the incoming components can vary over several radians, even if the frequency separation is quite small. Signals which occupy a bandwidth greater than that over which spectral components are affected in a similar way will become distorted, because the amplitudes and phases of the various spectral components in the received version of the signal are not the same as they were in the transmitted version. The phenomenon is known as *frequency selective fading*; the band over which the spectral components are affected in a similar way is known as the *coherence bandwidth*.

Figure 5.14 attempts to explain the situation. Here we have three possible Rayleigh power spectral density functions, as in Figure 5.8, but now delayed in ume relative to each other, as the principal scatters are markedly spaced in distance, those furthest away giving rise to the greatest excess path delay.

However, all the scattering comes from the source, say the base station, and hence the signal power has to be distributed among the three cases. In practice, the situation is much more like Figure 5.15. The Doppler shift of every component remains the same, that is f_d or less, but the spectral envelope will be a function of the particular environment. Also one can only describe a *delay spread* **s**, rather than a particular delay.

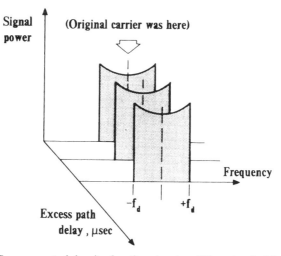

Figure 5.14 Power spectral density function showing different path delays

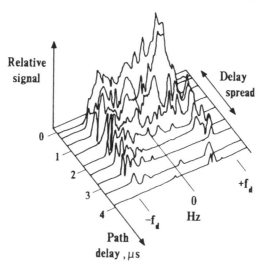

Figure 5.15 Typical scattered power profile in a suburban environment

The coherence bandwidth is inversely proportional to the delay spread. Therefore, a large delay spread (in microseconds, say) signifies a small coherence bandwidth (of the order of some 100 kHz), and manifests itself in the form of frequency selective fading for wideband type signals.

Extreme values of average delay and delay spread occur quite frequently in suburban areas; they are most common in environments with high-rise residential buildings, for example, irrespective of street orientations. Urban areas show comparable extreme values, though less frequently in the case of the delay spread. The outer fringe of the urban environment often represents the worst multipath, being influenced to a greater extent by remote tall buildings, or hills, some distance away. The effects of irregular scattering are also evident in the statistical distributions for the coherence bandwidths. Variability of the parameters is greater in suburban areas, although the extreme values are comparable.

This type of large scale characterization can be applied to the evaluation of radio systems and performance criteria emerge in terms of the percentage of locations where the performance requirements are achieved. In digital cellular radio such performance measures are laid down for multipath worst-case conditions development and testing.

Further reading

Jakes, W.C. (Ed.) (1974). *Microwave Mobile Communications,* Wiley Interscience, NY

Lee, W.C.Y. (1982). *Mobile Communications Engineering,* McGraw-Hill Book Co, NY

Parsons, J.D. (1992). *The Mobile Radio Propagation Channel,* Pentech Press, London

Rohner, C. (1996).'Fundamentals of radio network planning', Rohde & Schwarz, Antenna Seminar, April

6 Modulation Techniques

6.1 Introduction

Modulation is the process whereby message information is added to the radio carrier. The carrier wave was depicted in Figure 2.1. This is the carrier which attempts to get to and from the mobile, subject to the propagation losses and multipath effects described earlier. Adding modulation widens the bandwidth of the signal. Ideally, a carrier has no bandwidth, but in practice, drift, noise and propagation produce observable bandwidth. Modulation produces sidebands, either on one side, or on both sides of the nominal carrier frequency, usually having a distribution of amplitude over the assigned bandwidth. In effect one could say that whatever the modulation, the situation will exist in which one has a concentrated group of closely knit carriers, or signals, coming to and going from the mobile, *whether one specifies analog, or digital modulation.*

The question that one needs to ask, or solve, is what is the best way of arranging this group of signals; analog frequency modulation (FM), or continuous phase minimum shift keying (MSK), for example? Up until recently, narrowband FM has dominated the cellular market.

However, the world is moving to digital operation because of the ease of digital circuit implementation, and the fact that the control and switching between users can be performed much better by digital operation. Why not use digital modulation throughout the system? Can the signalling group around the carrier be arranged as efficiently as in the case of FM? What one finds is the converging of all forms of modulation to form the transmitted signal package; the difference between analog and digital modulation to some extent being the more extensive use of digital signal processing prior to modulation and especially after demodulation in the digital case.

6.2 The bandwidth problem

The bandwidth problem arises because, either one divides the subscriber channels into a well defined *frequency division multiple access* (FDMA) arrangement, or one divides the users into a *time division multiple access* (TDMA) time slot arrangement, which requires that they transmit their information promptly, at well defined intervals within the total assigned bandwidth. Alternatively, an operator shares all the allocated bandwidth of the service between all the users wishing to gain access, by separately coding each user's access (to the whole band) on a *code division multiple access* (CDMA) basis. At the end of the day the outcome is really very similar as far as usability of spectrum is concerned, one is tempted to say.

In an FDMA system spectrum partitioning is arranged and, as shown in Figure 3.1, our user's carrier assignment and cluster of modulation sidebands need to be accurately placed in the assigned channel. Sidebands at the edge of the assigned channel are required to be at least 60 dB below the unmodulated carrier amplitude.

This situation applies whether the modulation system is analog or digital. For example, if the system allocation is on a 25 kHz channel basis, it is clear that whatever the modulation the actual *message bandwidth* Δf_m needs to be less than the *channel assignment bandwidth* Δf_a; for example, if Δf_a = 25 kHz, then Δf_m is usually equal to 13 kHz.

To some extent it could be suggested much of the radio spectrum is being wasted because of channelization. A way around the problem is of course to assign channels on a staggered space-dispersed basis. In CDMA and TDMA the users are grouped in fewer wider channels and the waste problem is reduced. However, more signalling overhead is required, delayed multipath and near-far problems can arise.

In digital modulation a reduced bit rate per Hertz gives the possibility of having more data (user) channels. Unfortunately, for speech this is not easily achieved in practice, as described in the next chapter, and the necessary channel bandwidth remains a definite problem.

In Chapter 10 a simple guide formula for the number of radio subscribers, in a province or city, who can expect to be offered a service at any particular time, is derived, using the variables:

Area of the city considered = A km^2
Population of the city = P thousands of people
Average radius of a radio cell = R km
Number of radio channels in each cell = n_c

n_c will depend on how the cell repeat pattern is organized and also on the spectrum allocated to the service. Chapter 3 and, in particular Table 3.1, will be useful; channel allocation is discussed there.

It turns out that the percentage of the population in a city is given by the equation

$$\% = \frac{An_c}{PR^2} \tag{6.1}$$

The result can be rewritten involving the total bandwidth ΔF allocated to the service, the bandwidth assigned or allocated to each user Δf_a, and cell cluster size N, since

$$n_c = \frac{\Delta F}{\Delta f_a N} \qquad (6.2)$$

Hence

$$\% = \frac{A\Delta F}{PR^2 \Delta f_a N} \qquad (6.3)$$

This equation shows that, apart from the global terms, the success of a cellular arrangement depends on the spectrum allocated per user, that is, the term Δf_a, which as we saw above is greater than the signal bandwidth Δf_m.

Since the above equation, as explained later in Chapter 10, is an approximation, because of the trunking gain factor, population distribution factor, and also Δf_m is a percentage of Δf_a, usually only = 50%, this implies that we can use Δf_m (the user's signal modulation bandwidth) as the benchmark of any system design.

This question of spectral efficiency in a cell-structured radio system is discussed in detail later, also considering co-channel interference which, as discussed in section 3.4.2, is a problem centred around the cell layout geometry (N) and the co-channel interference threshold. 25 kHz analog FM is good in this respect, because it achieves a significant demodulation gain, but digital modulations are found to possess lower thresholds and smaller cell clusters are possible. However, if matters are pushed too far the total site co- and adjacent channel interference become the limiting factors, rather than the cell cluster arrangement.

6.3 Analog modulation bandwidths

Conventional frequency modulation is the mainstay of present-day mobile radio and analog cellular systems; it is an established technology, and certainly 12.5 kHz FM compactly occupies the signal bandwidth Δf_m for the transmission of speech, although 25 kHz FM has generally superior sound quality, for example, as on TACS and AMPS cellular. For completeness, we repeat some well-known factors associated with FM.

The FM signal waveform can be written

$$s(t)_{FM} = \cos(w_c + \beta m'(t))t \qquad (6.4)$$

where β = *modulation index* of analog FM

$$= \frac{\text{maximum frequency deviation}}{\text{modulation frequency}}$$

$$= \frac{\Delta f}{f_m} \qquad (6.5)$$

To generate FM it is necessary to cause frequency deviation of the transmitter output frequency, this being the so-called *instantaneous carrier frequency* f_i. In order to have a stable transmitter oscillator, it is essential to minimize its deviation, but if the oscillator is only a submultiple of the final output frequency, multiplication of the carrier can be used to generate the desired frequency and correct FM index, more accurately.

Figure 6.1 shows how the carrier waveform changes in frequency, but is transmitted with a constant amplitude. Note also how the FM has a non-regular zero crossing, meaning that the carrier changes phase over the modulation cycle.

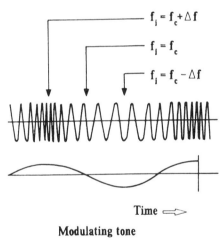

$$f_i = f_c + \Delta f$$
$$f_i = f_c$$
$$f_i = f_c - \Delta f$$

Time ⟹

Modulating tone

Figure 6.1 The instantaneous frequency of an FM waveform in relation to sinusoidal modulation

The spectrum shown in Figure 6.2 widens as the deviation (Δf) increases and the FM package can be viewed as a group of symmetrically packed sidebands. The operation with a voice message is such that the FM signal spectrum appears to occupy the same bandwidth for all speech, depending on the level at the microphone. To help in this matter a considerable amount of speech processing is carried out ahead of the modulation; namely clipping, filtering and pre-emphasis. A typical FM audio circuit arrangement is shown in Figure 6.3.

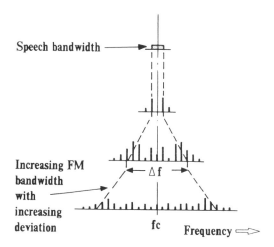

Figure 6.2 The corresponding spectrum of an FM waveform showing how the number of sidebands (equal spacing) increases with the modulation index

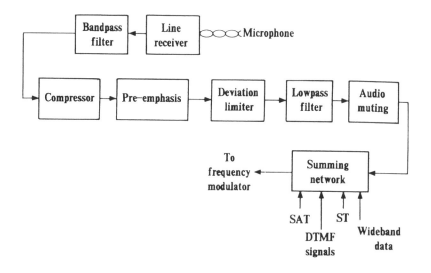

Figure 6.3 Schematic diagram of a typical cellular radio transmitter audio processing arrangement

The transmitter deviation is set to some maximum value, dictated by the agreed channel bandwidth. Table 6.1 shows three cases; the values being calculated from (6.5) and the notes appended to the table.

Apart from the bandwidth occupied by the FM waveform, column (3), the other interesting result is the improvement in the received signal-to-noise ratio on reception (and de-emphasis). Large index and hence wideband FM is clearly superior, but this result does not come without the penalty of worsening threshold. Figure 6.4 helps here. The improvement is only realized beyond a minimum threshold C/N ratio. Calling C/N the carrier-to-interference ratio C_i in cellular, one can now see why TACS and AMPS are limited to seven-cell clusters (see Figure 3.13). The narrowband NMT and NAMPS systems may tolerate four-cell clusters and hence serve more users, but the subscriber will generally have to accept a lower voice quality.

Table 6.1 Low index FM performance data

FM index	Δf kHz (1)	No. of sidebands (2)	Carson BW kHz (3)	S/N improvement at receiver (4)
0.8	2.4	4	10.8	+ 5 dB
1.5	4.5	6	15.0	+ 11 dB
5.0	15.0	12	36.0	+ 21 dB

Notes (1) Using $\Delta f = bf_m$ where $f_m = 3$ kHz
(2) Calculated from significant BW
(3) Using BW $= 2\Delta f + 2f_m$
(4) According to demodulation improvement and pre-emphasis textbook equations

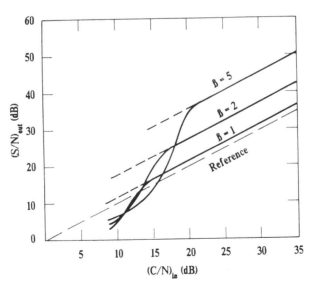

Figure 6.4 FM S/N output performance versus input C/N for different index modulations

An alternative analog modulation is double-sideband reduced, or suppressed carrier amplitude modulation (DSB-SC), which is an example of a modulation where the signal bandwidth fully fills the available bandwidth. Its signal-to-noise performance is as good as, if not better than 1.5 index FM, yet it only occupies less than 6 kHz bandwidth. It is referred to here because the principle of generation leads directly into digital modulation.

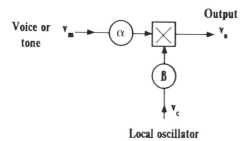

Figure 6.5 Generation of DSB-SC using a balanced mixer and showing dc offset components

Thus, Figure 6.5 shows how DSB-SC is generated using a double-balanced modulator, or multiplier. In practice, complete voltage balance of the signal input ports is not achieved, and the equation of operation of a practical modulator, including the dc offset components α and β, should be written as

$$v_o(t) = v_m(t) \, . \, v_c(t)$$

$$= (v_m \sin w_m t + \alpha) \, . \, (v_c \sin w_c t + \beta)$$

$$= v_m.v_c \sin w_m t \sin w_c t + \alpha.\beta + \alpha.v_c \sin w_c t + \beta.v_m \cos w_m t \qquad (6.6)$$

The desired output is the first product. Mixer imbalance and any non-linearity will cause difficulty with practical modulator realization, especially when the outputs of two quadrature mixers are added together, as is done below.

The waveform of DSB-SC is shown in Figure 6.6(e) below when describing digital phase shift keying modulation. The fully filtered PSK waveform will have sidebands as single pairs if a continuous on/off waveform is the modulation.

6.4 Shift key modulations

Digital modulation leads to a family of what are known as shift key modulations. Let us assume that the binary data is coded in some suitable form, such that a '1' or mark waveform $= +1$

a '0' or space waveform $= -1$

[over the symbol period T_b i.e. Figure 6.6]

6.4.1 *Phase shift keying*

Applying this signal to the balanced modulator of Figure 6.5, with the amendments shown in Figure 6.6, leads to binary phase shift keying (BPSK), or bipolar ASK, that is

$$s(t) = \pm \cos w_c t \tag{6.7}$$

The output waveform shown in Figure 6.6(d) has a constant amplitude, but a phase change of 180° at each mark/space transition. The spectrum of this waveform extends well beyond the symbol rate frequency f_r, where

$$f_r = 1/T_b$$

offset either side from the (suppressed) centre carrier, f_c.

Note that we will now be using symbol rate, as opposed to bit rate, in order to accommodate multilevel modulations, to be discussed below, but for binary modulation, either can be used.

To contain the spectrum, shaping or filtering of the data symbols has to be employed, see Figure 6.6(e).

The ideal Nyquist maximum signalling rate in a bandpass channel filter of bandwidth B is

$$f_r = B$$

Vestigial shaping of the channel filter would most likely be employed, which reduces f_r to the value

$$f_r = \frac{B}{1+\alpha} \tag{6.8}$$

where $\quad 0 < \alpha < 1$

(ideal)   (raised cosine)

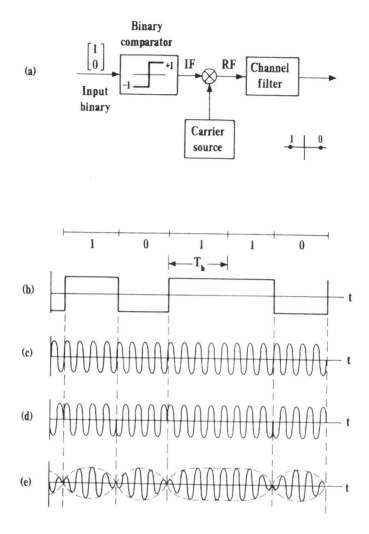

Figure 6.6 Generation of the binary phase shift keyed signal, (a) modulator, (b) data
waveform, (c) carrier, (d) unfiltered BPSK, (e) filtered BPSK

A change in the filtered envelope amplitude of the signal, shown in Figure
6.6(e), is seen to occur at the mark/space transition, and therefore more
complex quadrature modulation is used, as described below. In fact, the aim of a
digital modulation for cellular was to have a waveform with a *constant
envelope*, i.e., Figure 6.6(d). This plan has now been relaxed somewhat because
some envelope variation, which precludes a class C output RF amplifier, allows
a more 'efficient' modulation, as described below.

6.4.2 *Frequency shift keying*

Frequency shift keying (FSK) implies that one switches from a mark frequency to a space frequency, in sympathy with the data, see Figure 6.7.

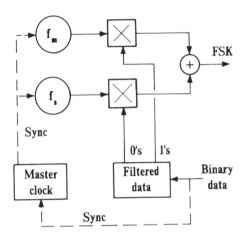

Figure 6.7 Schematic for generating FSK

The spectrum of the FSK waveform

$$s(t) = \cos (w_c \pm \Delta w)t \qquad\qquad (6.9)$$

can be calculated in the case of a regular 1,0,1,0 pattern, by adding the spectrum of the symbol rate-time limited carrier waveforms

$f_m = f_c - \Delta f$ for period T_b

$f_s = f_c + \Delta f$ for period T_b

One finds that the signal energy concentrates at the mark and space frequencies, as indicated in Figure 6.8.

The modulation index of FSK is given by

$$m = (f_s - f_m).T_b = \frac{f_s - f_m}{f_r} \qquad\qquad (6.10)$$

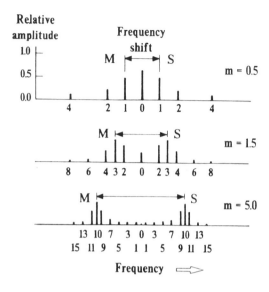

Figure 6.8 FSK signal spectrum with increasing deviation

To increase the data transmission rate, but not the bandwidth occupied, low index FSK schemes must be employed. A common standard is *fast frequency shift keying* (FFSK) where, at the baseband frequencies

$$f_m = 1200 \text{ Hz} \qquad \text{(note the nominal carrier}$$
$$f_s = 1800 \text{ Hz} \qquad \text{frequency } f_c = 1500 \text{ Hz})$$
$$f_b = 1200 \text{ bps, } = \text{symbol rate frequency} = f_r$$

$$\therefore m = \frac{1800 - 1200}{1200} = 0.5$$

Here one cycle of 1200 Hz is followed by one and a half cycles of 1800 Hz, with no phase discontinuity at the bit interval. The spectrum is now concentrated in the band 600 to 2400 Hz.

It can be shown that FFSK is equivalent to *minimum shift keying* (MSK), a particular form of *quadrature phase shift keying* (QPSK), which is described below. The waveform of this modulation is sketched in Figure 6.9. It is useful to refer to this diagram when reading about MSK and the phasor diagram in Figure 6.13.

Figure 6.9 Detail of the fast frequency shift (and minimum shift) keying waveform

With all three of these modulations, however, the modulation signal has significant adjacent channel sideband components, which make them unsuitable for digital cellular radio systems where good adjacent channel performance is an essential requirement, e.g., see section 3.4.3 earlier.

The solution to the difficulty is to shape the binary signal waveform by suitable wave filtering. In the case of FSK, the conventional method is to constrain the changeover from a mark to a space, with a filter in the data source, as in Figure 6.7.

The coherence between the mark and space tone is retained by arranging that

$$f_m = f_c - nf_b/4 \qquad \text{where } n = \text{an integer}$$

$$f_s = f_c + nf_b/4 \qquad\qquad\qquad\qquad (6.11)$$

where

$$f_b = \text{bit rate (same as the symbol rate } f_r \text{ here)}$$

When $n = 1$, we have FFSK as just described. When $n = 2$, we have again, coherent FSK, with $m = 1$. FFSK can only be demodulated with a coherent demodulator; FSK with $m = 1$ can be detected with a non-coherent demodulator, but there is a penalty to pay with regard to the BER performance. However, the mark/space coherence achieved by observing the rules in (6.11), which defines *coherent frequency exchange keying* (CFEK), provides superior adjacent channel performance over and above simple FSK, as shown in Figure 6.10.

The data throughput can be increased by using more than two frequencies. Thus using L levels, or frequencies, a symbol can represent $\log_2 L$ bits; that is, four frequencies will convey two bits per symbol. This technology is implemented in the new European radio messaging (paging) system (ERMES).

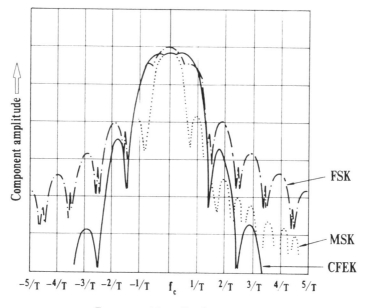

Frequency either side of carrier

Figure 6.10   The adjacent and in-band spectrum occupancy non-coherent of FSK
                    (m = 1), MSK (m = 0.5) and CFEK (m = 1)

The data rate specified is 6.25 kbps; it thus only requires a symbol rate of 3.125 kbps (half), and uses the four signalling frequencies

$$f_{00} = f_c - 3f_b/2; \qquad \text{offset} = -4687.5 \text{ Hz}$$
$$f_{10} = f_c - f_b/2; \qquad \text{offset} = -1562.5 \text{ Hz}$$
$$f_{11} = f_c + f_b/2; \qquad \text{offset} = +1562.5 \text{ Hz}$$
$$f_{01} = f_c + 3f_b/2; \qquad \text{offset} = +4687.5 \text{ Hz}$$

The arrangement is a four-level equivalent of the two-level CFEK, with m = 1.0; at least between adjacent levels.

The data is shaped using a 10th order Bessel filter, with a 3 dB point at 4 kHz, so that the carrier oscillator can move smoothly from one signalling frequency to the next within the symbol period, that is, a frequency change of 1/3.125 msec, as sketched in Figure 6.11. It is claimed that adjacent channel interference levels of better than −70 dB can be achieved and a *modulation efficiency* of approximately 1.3 bps/Hz is offered. A three-level, conventional limiter-discriminator detector can be used, provided that the signal receiving conditions are good.

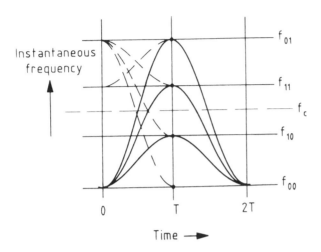

Figure 6.11   The possible instantaneous frequency positions of 4-level FSK over two symbol periods

6.4.3 Modulation efficiency

It is perhaps important to deviate from the main discourse to amplify the meaning of the modulation efficiency factor. It really stems from the Nyquist transmission rate described right at the beginning in section 6.4.1. The results are set out in Table 6.2. One begins with the Nyquist ideal lowpass filter case, which can just sustain a data transmission rate of 2 × the filter bandwidth, = 2 B. However, on a radio channel one is dealing with a bandpass filter case, and the rate drops to B. If B = 1 Hz, the ideal rate is clearly 1 bps. The ideal case can only be approached, i.e., vestigial filtering reduces the rate by $(1 + \alpha)$. This means that for any binary modulation the modulation efficiency will be less than 1 bps/Hz. To improve matters one may use a *multi-level* modulation, where L = 2, 4, 8, . . . The modulation efficiency now increases by the factor $\log_2 L$, as indicated in Table 6.2.

Table 6.2 Nyquist transmission rates

System	Transmission Rate
Ideal LPF with BPSK	2 B
Ideal BPF with BPSK	B
Cosine squared BPSK	$\dfrac{B}{2}$
Vestigial BPF BPSK	$\dfrac{2}{1+\alpha}$
Vestigial BPF QPSK	$\dfrac{2B}{1+\alpha}$
Vestigial BPF 16L - PSK	$\dfrac{4B}{1+\alpha}$

6.4.4 Quadrature phase shift keying

As described for FSK, so four phase levels will provide two data bits per symbol in a phase shift keying scheme. Thus four phase *quadrature* PSK (QPSK) provides twice the data throughput in the same bandwidth when compared to BPSK. On the other hand QPSK needs two 90° offset multipliers, as shown in Figure 6.12, each acting as a binary PSK modulator, as in Figure 6.6.

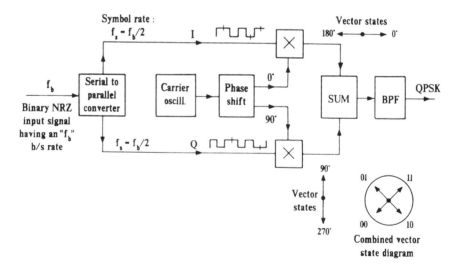

Figure 6.12 The two-path method of generating QPSK

As shown in the diagram of QPSK generation, each symbol is formed by two data bits, which causes the resultant quadrature carrier signal addition to come to rest at 45° intervals around the phase diagram, shown as an insert in Figure 6.12. This combined vector state diagram shows where the signal phase is at the centre of each symbol period. The bandwidth required for transmission of QPSK can in theory be $0.5f_b$, but to allow for filtering as described above, and below, the bandwidth is increased to $0.7f_b$ in practice. This represents a modulation efficiency of 1.4 bps/Hz as compared to an ideal modulation efficiency of 2 bps/Hz.

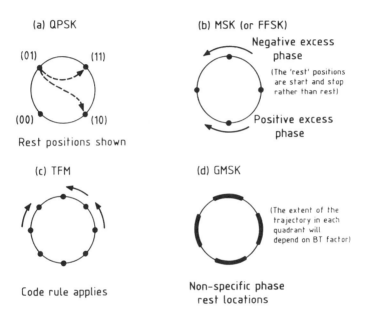

Figure 6.13   The movement of the carrier phasor during digital modulation signalling for the four modulations, QPSK, MSK, TFM and GMSK

Looking at the phase diagram of QPSK, the interesting question is what happens as one moves from one symbol (say 01) to the next (say 11). If there is no coherence between the data rate and the carrier frequency the waveform may well be constrained to move across the phase circle, or rapidly round the circle, shown now in Figure 6.13(a). However, by combining off-set PSK in the lower path (Q) of the QPSK modulator, Figure 6.12, with shaping of the data pulses so that they follow a half-sine waveform profile, the modified QPSK waveform, now called *minimum shift keying* (MSK), acquires a constant envelope and continuous phase waveform, in fact equivalent to FFSK, as discussed in section 6.4.2 above.

6.4.5 *Minimum shift keying*

Minimum shift keying achieves the objective of having the carrier move from
one phase state to the next, around the phase circle, as shown in Figure 6.13(b)
in $\pi/2$ increments. To do this the frequency must either be ahead of the nominal
carrier frequency, or behind; that is, either f_s or f_m. For FFSK, the shift of the
carrier frequency is ± 300 Hz, that is, one quarter the bit rate. The so-called
frequency deviation f_s to f_m (600 Hz) is equal to half the bit rate (1200 bps),
giving m = 0.5. However, MSK still suffers from relatively poor adjacent
channel sidebands due to its FSK-type spectrum.

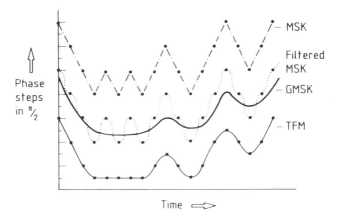

Figure 6.14   The phase movement with time as a function of the data for MSK, filtered
MSK, TFM and GMSK

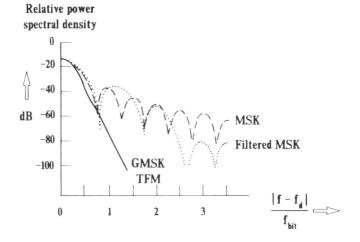

Figure 6.15   The adjacent channel power spectral density of MSK, filtered MSK, TFM
and GMSK

The way forward is to constrain this change of frequency by filtering to improve the situation. The diagram Figure 6.14 demonstrates the point. The sudden switch in frequency, from say f_m to f_s, which causes the phase to move by $\pi/2$ radians in a symbol period, is smoothed out and some improvement on the out-of-channel power spectral density results, which is illustrated in Figure 6.15.

For much greater improvement, but still retaining the important bandwidth efficient constant envelope property, two approaches have been developed.

6.4.6 Tamed frequency shift keying

The approach here is to code the data stream correlatively so that fewer and smaller phase changes take place. The code rule proposed established that a change of phase by $\pi/2$ only takes place if the three succeeding bits have the same polarity; while no phase change takes place if the three bits are of alternating polarity. Polarity changes of $\pi/4$ are reserved for the bit configurations 110, 100, 011 and 001. The result is a much more constrained movement around the phase circle, as depicted in Figure 6.13, and in Figure 6.14, with a correspondingly much improved spectral performance. This also accounts for the name, *tamed* FM (TFM). It must be recognized, however, that the phase rest positions are now placed at $\pi/4$ angles around the phase circuit, which must be taken into account in the receiver demodulator design.

6.4.7 Gaussian minimum shift keying

The classical theory of impulse transmission shows that transmitting at the Nyquist rate $f_r = B$, is *intersymbol interference* (ISI) free, because the ideal impulse response has regular zero crossings. Increasing the channel bandwidth to allow full cosine roll-off (twice bandwidth) retains the impulse shape, but also makes the far-off oscillations attenuate very rapidly. A compromise is to have a Gaussian-shaped filter, as depicted in Figure 6.16. This will generate a likewise Gaussian-shaped impulse response.

There is some ISI at the first zero crossing time, but very little beyond. Thus a Gaussian-shaped filter, Figure 6.16, having the same envelope shape,

$$A(f) = \exp^{-0.54} (f/f_c)^2 \tag{6.12}$$

produces a response which has only 1% ISI, but considerably better adjacent channel performance.

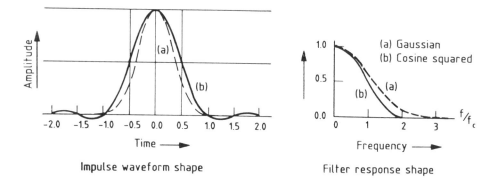

Figure 6.16   The impulse response of, (a) a Gaussian low-pass filter and (b) raised cosine-shaped LPF, shown as insert

Gaussian pulse pre-shaping can be added to the previous modulation MSK and is then termed *Gaussian* MSK (GMSK). The pulse shape after a Gaussian filter is also Gaussian, hence some ISI remains. One has a choice between the pre-modulation filter bandwidth B and the bit period T. If B > 1/T, then the waveform is essentially MSK; if, however, B < 1/T, the change of symbol cannot reach its next position in the time allotted. The effect is shown in Figure 6.13(d), when B < 1/T. The constellation becomes blurred due to the influence of remnants of previous pulses on the phase change. The phase behaviour attempts to follow the $\pi/2$ positions, as in Figure 6.14, but is constrained. In the receiver a complementary Gaussian filter will recover the data because it will again be influenced by the predesigned intersymbol interference. It does mean however that the phase modulation pattern must be generated accurately, otherwise the phase pattern cannot be interpreted. A BT product, = 0.3, as BT is denoted in the business, is used for GSM. GSM, as will be discussed below, operates with a bit rate of 270.833 kbps in a 200 kHz channel. This implies a modulation efficiency of 1.35 bps/Hz, that is, the bandwidth is just 0.74 times the bit channel rate, as expected for filtered QPSK.

It is also worth noting the so-called trellis diagram of these phase shift keyed modulations, shown in Figure 6.17. In the case of MSK, phase changes of $\pi/2$ occur at each data interval. All 1's cause the phase to move upwards at 45°; all 0's downwards at –45°. Other patterns will form the trellis.

In the case of GMSK, depending on the BT product value, the phase change is unable to follow the MSK trellis. This is why in the GSM signalling protocol, as described in Chapter 9, a burst data mode is used in order to maintain a phase reference, which would become lost after a long string of 1's or 0's on their own.

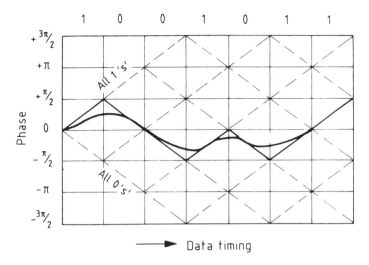

Figure 6.17 The trellis diagram of the carrier phase positions formed by data changes during MSK and GMSK modulation

Because MSK and GMSK are akin to FFSK, a more straightforward way of generating GMSK is to use a voltage-controlled oscillator (VCO), but in order to maintain the required phase and frequency, the VCO is embedded in a phase locked loop circuit, as shown in Figure 6.18.

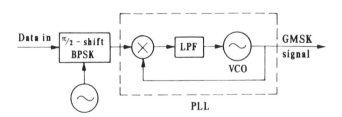

Figure 6.18 Phase locked loop construction for generating GMSK

The date is first shifted by $\pi/2$ using the mixer circuit of Figure 6.5. The loop now contains a Gaussian LPF which has a transfer function of the form

$$h(t) = \frac{\sqrt{\pi}}{\alpha} \exp \left\{ -\frac{\pi}{\alpha} t \right\}^2 \qquad (6.13)$$

i.e. the inverse of eqn 6.12, where

$$\alpha = \frac{\sqrt{2\ln 2}}{B} = \frac{1.1774}{B} \qquad\qquad (6.14)$$

The bit period in GSM, we shall find is 48/13 μs, which is a rate of 270.833 kbps, so the filter 3 dB bandwidth is chosen to be 81.25 kHz, i.e. BT = 0.3.

The frequency deviation is optional in this circuit, however. The modulation index m, eqn 6.10, needs to be set to m = 0.5, for GMSK, since it is a minimum shift keying scheme.

For other less rigorous mobile radio services, a larger deviation index may be employed, as the waveform then becomes easier to detect, i.e. demodulation. When m> 0.5, one now has what is known as *Gaussian frequency shift key modulation* (GFSK).

GFSK does not have such a stringent spectral occupancy as GMSK. However, GMSK is not without its difficulty, as Figure 6.19 demonstrates.

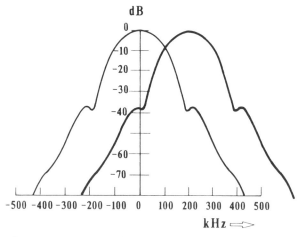

Figure 6.19   The spectrum of two adjacent GSM channels transmitting 0.3 BT GMSK, each in their allocated 200 kHz channel

Although the out-of-band energy roll-off is good (beginning at ± 100 kHz from the centre frequency), there is still considerable energy in the immediate adjacent channel (–40 dB or more). At two channels away the situation is clearly good, however.

Measurements confirm that the power spectral density of GMSK does indeed exceed that of MSK in respect of adjacent channel performance and a better out-of-band performance ratio can be achieved. GMSK is also in theory a constant amplitude waveform; unfortunately, the fact that the carrier must be power controlled and also confined to timed bursts, implies that the overall carrier envelope will possess some spectral spreading when using class-C transmitter stages.

6.4.8 Differential phase shift keying

As we noted when discussing the generation of QPSK, Figure 6.12, a rectangular bit stream leaves one with a phase circle diagram with specific rest positions at the 45° corners, the actual carrier waveform exchanging phase at each symbol period. If the following coding scheme is used

Message symbol	00	01	10	11
Phase change	0°	−90°	+90°	180°

the signal space diagram shown in Figure 6.20(a) will be observed. The signal waveform must at intervals pass through zero, which is of course very difficult to amplify accurately, especially within a transmitter.

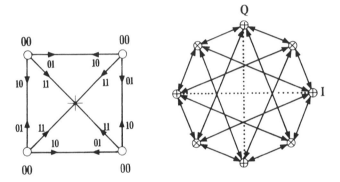

Figure 6.20   Signal space diagrams for QPSK, (a) conventional, (b) π/4 differential constellation

Also it has the disadvantage that for the symbol 00 there is no phase change and the signal vector will rest at one of the nodes.

If differential encoding is applied to the data stream, such rest positions do not occur because the transmitted data is differential. Differential encoding applied to binary PSK is shown in Figure 6.21. If this scheme is now applied to QPSK generation, as in Figure 6.22, and made four-level, as shown, a totally new signal space diagram is formed, which is constructed in Figure 6.20(b).

This uses the coding rule:

Message symbol	00	01	10	11
Phase change	−45°	−135°	+45°	+135°

and the constellation pattern shown in Figure 6.20(b) comes about. The carrier vector now has no rest position; nor does it pass through zero. Some amplitude variation does occur and quasi-linear amplification is necessary in what is now called π/4 DQPSK modulation.

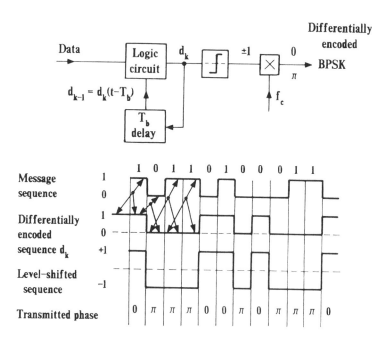

Figure 6.21 Differential encoding applied to form DPSK modulator

This is the modulation adopted for the 800 MHz North American digital cellular schemes.. Here a raised cosine-shaped filtered π/4 shifted DQPSK system is used. A transmission rate of 48.6 kbps in a channel spacing of 30 kHz will be described below, which gives a spectrum efficiency of 1.62 bps/Hz, a 20% improvement over GSM, which has come about as a result of relaxing the stringent requirement of a constant envelope modulation, i.e. Figure 6.6.

As may be well known, it is practical to generate a multi-level PSK waveform, either having the phase reference positions placed symmetrically around a circle in the signal space diagram (M-ary PSK), or quaternary amplitude shift keying waveform (QAM).

Because, as was discussed earlier, multipath propagation becomes much more disruptive on multi-level modulations, they have so far not usually been considered suitable for cellular schemes; hence M-ary modulations, where M > 4, will not be discussed, at least for foreseeable FDMA or TDMA schemes.

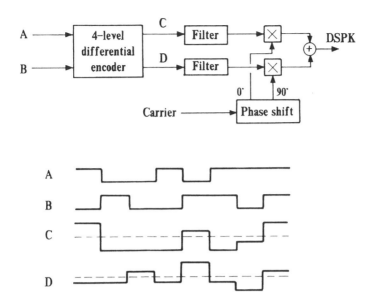

Figure 6.22 Four-level differential encoding applied to a QPSK modulator so as to generate $\pi/4$ DQPSK

6.5 Bit error rate

Digital modulation does not suffer an apparent worsening S/N ratio, as does analog modulation since, as explained in Chapter 1, digits become misinterpreted and an increasing bit error rate (BER) response sets in. The probability of an error being recorded, when judged against the received carrier-to-noise ratio, can be calculated by considering the error region surrounding the signal vector. Thus Figure 6.23 shows the signal vector space for QPSK and in particular the signal vector (11).

An interfering signal $V_i \geq \sqrt{2} \times V_c$ will clearly cause the symbol to be misinterpreted. One can compute (with some difficulty) the probability of making an error versus the carrier-to-noise ratio C/N, but it is more efficient to express C/N as the ratio of the E_b/N_b as follows:

Let carrier power C = energy per bit $E_b \times$ rate R, $(= f_b)$

noise power N = noise power per Hertz $N_o \times B$, $(= BW)$

$$\therefore \frac{C}{N} = \frac{E_b}{N_o} \times \frac{R}{B}$$

Cellular Radio

or $$\frac{E_b}{N_o} = \frac{C}{N} \times \frac{B}{R}$$ (6.15)

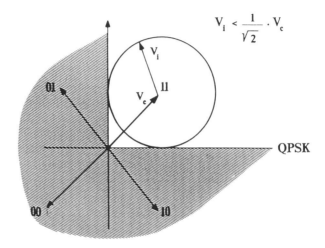

Figure 6.23 A QPSK signal vector space in the presence of an interfering vector

The bit error probability P_e then has the general form:

$$P_e = \frac{1}{2}\mathrm{erfc}\left(\frac{E_b}{N_o}\right)^{\frac{1}{2}}$$ (6.16)

The shape of P_e versus E_b/N_o is also shown in Figure 6.24.

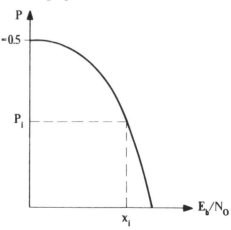

Figure 6.24 General shape of digital transmission BER in a white noise environment

A specific comparison of BPSK and QPSK (which is 4-level PSK) is interesting, because as shown in Figure 6.25, QPSK is some 3 dB worse in performance than BPSK. However, the bit rate is twice, in the case of QPSK, so that if only *additive white Gaussian noise* (AWGN) was the cause of errors, multi-level modulations would perform as well as two-level binary modulation.

In mobile radio several other sources of channel imperfection arise, however. Thus whereas in Figure 6.26 the theoretical result is shown, in practice, receiver and transmitter RF circuits are needed in the data transmission system, and also multipath will exist in the propagation environment. The observed BER worsens, as shown, and is often limited to some *irreducible* level. These three cases are marked laboratory, static and moving at 30 mph, in Figure 6.26, respectively; see also Figure 1.13.

These imperfections can easily amount to 6 dB or more. Carrier-to-noise ratio therefore needs to be this much higher to achieve the same BER.

When digital modulation schemes form part of a mobile system, multipath propagation causes further degradation in the system performance and necessitates channel sounding and path equalization techniques, which will be referred to in the following chapters.

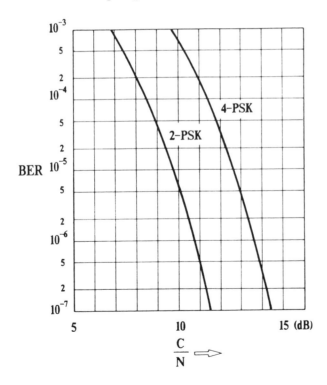

Figure 6.25 BER versus C/N for ideal PSK in an AWGN environment

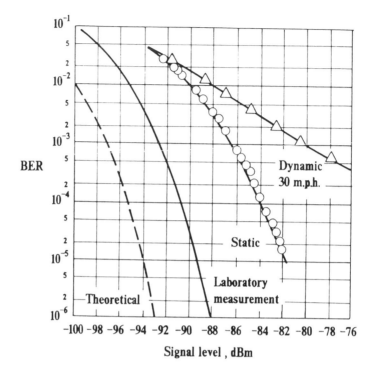

Figure 6.26   Expected and observed bit error rate performance for 2400 bps MSK over
a 12.5 kHz VHF radio channel at 172 MHz

6.5.1 Improving BER

Another important consideration in regard to digital modulation is the form of
demodulation. Coherent methods (which require recovery of the precise carrier
frequency and possibly phase) are generally superior to the more easily
implemented non-coherent circuit arrangement, such as an FM discriminator.
Figure 6.27 illustrates the point; for example, DPSK can offer approximately a
6 dB improvement at the more critical BER levels, such as BER = 1×10^{-3}.

From a digital cellular radio design point of view, BER versus C/N ratio is
clearly more relevant, more so than the received signal level in dBm. Recalling
(6.15), if C is expressed in dBm and using N = -174 dBm + 10 log B, plus
receiver noise figure F in dB, the ratio B/R will depend on the modulation
efficiency of the modulation and, as we can observe, a high efficiency
modulation will usually make the ratio E_b/N_o worse.

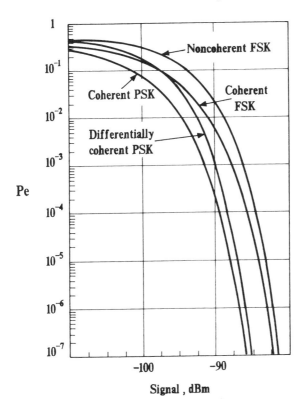

Figure 6.27 BER performance of four binary modulations versus relative signal level

Data errors can also be reduced, or corrected, by forward error correction (FEC) techniques. Unfortunately, FEC implies transmitting more data, which means, either (i) accepting more errors for the same throughput, or (ii) lowering the data transmission rate, or (iii) increasing the signal power. The last implication is contained in Shannon's formula

$$\frac{R}{B} < \log_{10} \left(1 + \frac{E_b R}{N_o B} \right) \qquad (6.17)$$

This says that if the bandwidth is limited, one can only increase the transmission rate provided that the minimum E_b/N_o ratio increases faster.

The way around the conflict is to combine the coding and modulation. The data message is now pre-coded before modulation in specific patterns, such as a set-partitioned code, and this code can be recognized with added confidence in the received signal. Hence, use of the code saves transmitter power on a per-data bit basis without increasing the signal bandwidth. *Coding gains* of up to 6 dB in E_b/N_o ratio have been predicted. So-called *trellis coding* leading to so-called *trellis code modulations* (TCM) are mainly used, based on the phase locations which are specific to MSK type of modulation indicated in Figure 6.17. Such strategies are put into place as part of the GSM system implementation construction.

Further reading

Alshamali, A. and Macario, R.C.V. (1994). 'Technical features of the planned European Radio Messaging System – ERMES', *IEEE Veh Tech Soc News*, August, pp 22-25

Bennett, W.R. and Davey, J.R. (1965). *Data Transmission,* McGraw-Hill Book Co, NY

Couch, L.E. (1993). *Digital and Analog Communication Systems,* Fourth Edition, Macmillan Inc., NY

de Jager, F. and Dekker, C.B. (1978). 'Tamed frequency modulation, a novel method to achieve spectrum economy in digital transmission', *IEEE Trans.,* COM-26, May, p. 534

Feher, K. (Ed) (1987). *Advanced Digital Communications,* Prentice-Hall, NJ

Feher, K. (1996). *Wireless Digital Communications, Modulation and Spread Spectrum Applications,* Prentice-Hall, NJ

IEEE J. Selected Area Comms, (1989). 'Bandwidth and power efficient coded modulation', Aug. and Dec. issues

Jenks, F.G., Morgan, P.D. and Warren, C.S. (1972). 'Use of four-level phase modulation for digital mobile radio', *IEEE Trans., EMC-14,* November, pp 113-128

Murota, K. and Hirade, K. (1981). 'GMSK modulation for digital mobile radio telephones', *IEEE Trans.,* COM-29, No. 7, July, p. 1044

Sklar, B. (1988). *Digital Communications; Fundamentals and Applications,* Prentice-Hall International, Inc, NY

Sunde, E.D. (1954). 'Theoretical fundamentals of pulse transmission', *BSTJ*, 33, May, p. 721 and Pt II, July, p. 987

Yoshihiko, Y. and Nagata, Y. (1987). 'Highly Efficient Digital Mobile Communications with a Linear Modulation Method', *IEEE Journal Comms.*, *SAC-5, No 5*, June, pp. 890-895

Ziemer, R.E. and Tranter, W.H. (1995). *'Principles of Communication Systems'*, Fourth Ed., John Wiley, USA

7 Speech Coding

7.1 Introduction

It is clearly necessary to find a way of digitizing speech if an all-digital cellular radio system is to be achieved.

Pulse Code Modulation (PCM) is now used throughout the fixed telephone network, being first introduced around 1962. Many studies have dealt with the standard 64 kbps PCM voice transmission hierarchy, which assumes 8 bits per sample at a sampling rate of 8000 samples per second. Using non-linear sampling improves the inherent signal-to-noise ratio so that a 64 kbps log-law PCM codec is a CCITT standard, known as G 711.

Speech coding has come a long way since the introduction of pulse code modulation. Present-day techniques seek to exploit the intrinsic properties of speech signals in order to remove redundancy and achieve good speech quality at much lower bit rates. This chapter is basically a brief introduction to speech coding, with emphasis being given to the encoding of narrowband telephone voice signals for network communication quality speech. The important coding techniques and achievements are discussed in the light of existing international coding standards.

7.2 Coding requirements

Speech coding algorithms are developed and optimized to satisfy a number of application specific requirements. Obviously, the quality of the recovered speech signal is a critical aspect in the design of the speech coding and decoding chain (codec). The objective signal-to-noise ratio (SNR) can assist in evaluating and comparing the performance of systems operating at relatively high bit rates (>16 kbps). However, when SNR measures are applied to intermediate and low bit rate codecs they often fail to correlate well with the *subjective* quality of the decoded speech signal. As a result various subjective tests are employed to quantify output speech quality, with the *mean opinion score* (MOS) test, scale (1 to 5), being the most popular.

When applied to narrowband telephone speech (300 Hz to 3400 Hz) an MOS score greater than or equal to 4.0 implies network quality speech, often referred to as 'toll' quality. An MOS value in the range of 3.5 to 4.0 corresponds to communication quality, and is characterized by some degradation, noticeable by a listener. Communication quality speech is acceptable in certain telephone applications, such as mobile radio and voice mail. MOS values in the region of 2.5 to 3.5 imply synthetic quality speech. This is to all intents and purposes intelligible, but with reduced naturalness and limited speaker recognizability. Synthetic quality is found in low bit rate (2.4 kbps) secure voice transmission systems.

The decoded speech quality is closely linked to two other coder design factors, namely output bit rate and coder complexity. In general, as the required bit rate decreases, codecs become more sophisticated and more complex in an attempt to retain high decoded speech quality. Obviously, algorithm complexity has a direct impact on implementation cost and power consumption. Nevertheless, speech coding quality deteriorates at lower bit rates and the challenge is to design efficient low bit rate, high speech quality, low complexity codecs. Figure 7.1 highlights speech quality as a function of output bit rate for the three classes of speech coding schemes, namely waveform coders, vocoders and hybrid systems. It is important to note that if several speech coders are connected in tandem, e.g. an intercontinental call, the speech quality could deteriorate below the value shown for the weakest codec.

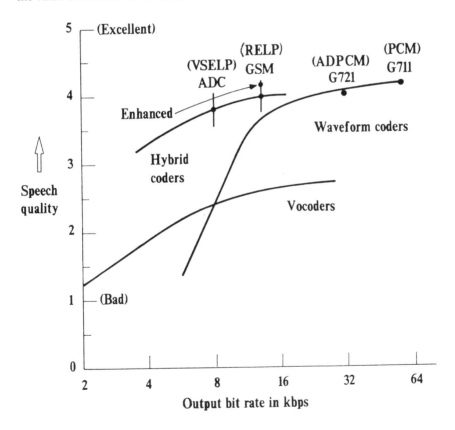

Figure 7.1 Speech quality versus bit rate for telephone bandwidth speech codecs

7.3 Coding techniques

7.3.1 Waveform coders

Speech coding algorithms have been developed for encoding what is termed telephone bandwidth speech, and can be classified into three categories. The first category consists of algorithms which attempt to reproduce, at the output of the decoder, a close approximation of the original speech signal. They are known as waveform coders and operate successfully at intermediate and high bit rates (2 to 8 bits/sample at a 8 kbps sampling rate). These coders are now briefly described.

Pulse code modulation: as already mentioned, the first waveform coding technique to be developed, consists of both time quantization (sampling) and amplitude quantization and, although of limited compression/quality capability, PCM is used today at 64 kbps, in both public and private 'fixed' telecommunication networks, in the form of the G711 CCITT standard, with an MOS score of 4.3. The amplitude quantizer (or simply the quantizer) is an important element present in all encoding systems.

Differential coders, on the other hand, form an error signal, as the difference between successive input speech samples and a corresponding prediction estimate, which is then quantized and transmitted. *Adaptive differential pulse code modulation* (ADPCM) and *adaptive predictive coding* (APC) represent two important intermediate bit rate (32 to 16 kbps) differential codecs. Both systems estimate the incoming input samples using previously decoded samples.

ADPCM employs a short-term predictor which partially models the speech spectral envelope. The predictor can be forward or backward adaptive, with its coefficients defined periodically (block adaptive), or at every sampling instant (sequentially adaptive).

The CCITT G721 ADPCM standard, introduced in 1984, achieves network quality speech (MOS score of 4.1) at 32 kbps. This is a low complexity codec of reasonable robustness, when operating with channel bit error rates in the range of 10^{-3} to 10^{-2}, and is therefore well suited for wireless access applications based on low power, handheld cordless telephones.

This standard has been extended in recommendation G723 to operate at 24 and 40 kbps. In addition, an *embedded* ADPCM standard has been established by CCITT, which operates at 40, 32, 24 and 16 kbps and can be used in wideband packet network applications. Notice that because speech quality deteriorates considerably at bit rates below 32 kbps, noise shaping and post-filtering needs to be added to the codec in order to minimize the perceptual effect of quantization noise.

APC employs both short and long-term prediction in a differential coding structure. The system outperforms ADPCM at 16 kbps and offers communication quality speech at bit rates as low as 10 kbps. As with ADPCM, the introduction of noise shaping and post filtering in APC reduces the subjective loudness of the background quantization noise.

Delta modulation, that is, a one-bit PCM variant, in the form of *digitally variable slope delta modulation* (DVSDM) is used in one version of CT2 (a second generation UK cordless telephone) because of its lower implementation simplicity and cost, but to some extent voice quality is sacrificed.

7.3.2 Vocoders

The second class of speech coding techniques consists of algorithms called *vocoders* which attempt to describe the speech production mechanism in terms of a few independent parameters serving as the information-bearing signals.

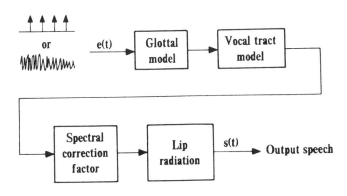

Figure 7.2 The source/filter model for speech

Vocoders consider that speech is produced from a 'source-filter' arrangement, such as set out in Figure 7.2. Voiced speech is the result of exciting the vocal tract (filter) with a series of quasi-periodic glottal pulses generated by the vocal cords (source). Unvoiced speech, on the other hand, is produced by exciting the filter with a random noise waveform. Vocoders then operate on the input signal, using an 'analysis' process based on a particular speech production model, and extract a set of source-filter parameters which are encoded and transmitted. At the receiver, they are decoded and used to control a speech synthesizer which corresponds to the model used in the analysis process. Provided that all the perceptually significant parameters are extracted, the synthesized signal, as perceived by the human ear, closely resembles the original speech signal.

The 'filter' part of the speech production model can be defined by operating in the time or frequency domain and effectively determines the 'envelope' information of the speech spectrum.

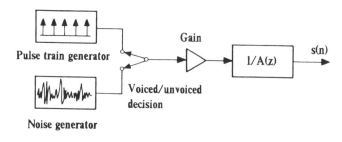

Figure 7.3 The encoding arrangement of the basic vocoder

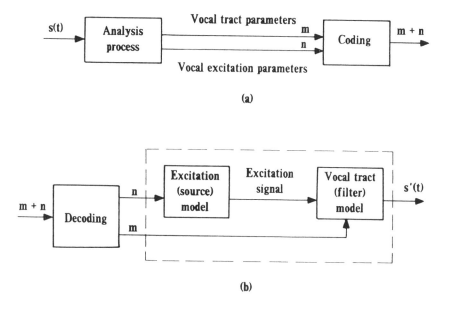

Figure 7.4 Generalized block diagram of a vocoder system, (a) analysis at the transmitter, (b) synthesis process at the receiver

The most popular model in use today is the so-called *linear predictive coder* (LPC) and can be viewed as a multi-stage filter A(z) set up by a digital (time domain) algorithm. Figure 7.3 indicates how the vocal model of Figure 7.2 has been reduced to a single-filter function with either a pitch impulse generator for voiced frames, or a noise generator for unvoiced frames. The concept of frames enters in as the process cannot be carried out continuously, but in frames. We shall find that the frame time, in the cellular phone coders to be described, is 20 msec. The source voice power is set by the amplifier. This circuit represents the encoding side of the vocoder.

The digitized speech waveform now no longer needs to be transmitted from the speaker to the listener; all that is required are the parameters of the filter, the gain of the amplifier and when to use the voiced or unvoiced source. A generalized block diagram of a vocoder is shown in Figure 7.4.

Vocoders are medium complexity systems and operate at low bit rates, typically 2.4 kbps, with synthetic quality speech. Their poor quality speech is due to, (i) the oversimplified 'source' model used to drive the 'filter' and, (ii) the assumption that the source and the filter are linearly independent.

7.3.3 Hybrid coders

The poor and synthetic quality of speech vocoders has led to what is known as the *residual excitation* approach to speech coding, a concept whereby not all the speech is synthesized, but a small part is transmitted as a coded waveform part (of the original envelope), and as a vocoder part; hence the name hybrid. The penalty is the higher bit rate of transmission required, but now a very much improved speech quality is realized.

The system extracts a low frequency band from the input signal (typically 300 to 940 Hz) which is waveform coded and transmitted, in addition to the vocoder channel (filter information). This baseband signal, which contains the required excitation information, is processed at the receiving end by a non-linear element that flattens and broadens the signals spectrum, without affecting its periodicity (if any), to yield an improved excitation signal. However, the improved speech quality obtained from the voice excited channel vocoder (and from other residual excitation systems) is achieved only at the expense of several extra kbps needed to code the baseband (residual) signal.

Many residual excited hybrid coding systems have been proposed, most of them using linear predictive modelling of the synthesis filter. In particular, a *residual excited linear predictive* (RELP) coding system has been developed for low to intermediate bit rate (4.8 to 16 kbps) operation.

RELP systems employ short-term (and in certain cases, long-term) linear prediction, to formulate a difference signal (residual) in a feed-forward manner. Early systems used baseband coding and transmitted a lowpass version of the residual. The decoder recovered an approximation of the full-band residual signal, by employing high frequency regeneration which was subsequently used to synthesize output speech.

Multipulse-excitation linear predictive coder (MPE-LPC) systems model the excitation signal as a sequence of irregularly spaced pulses. MPE coders employ a synthesis filter which consists of one or two autoregressive (AR) filters in series. The first filter models the 'smooth' spectral envelope of the signal (short-term filter) while the second (if used) models the harmonic (fine) structure of the spectrum (long-term filter). The parameters of the excitation model (i.e. the pulse positions and amplitudes) and part of the synthesis filter (i.e. the long-term filter) are determined in a closed-loop optimization process.

An outline of an MPE decoder is shown in Figure 7.5. The multipulse excitation generator can be seen. Also shown is a block marked *long-term predictor* (LTP). Because the speech to be coded is divided up into segments (the 20 msec frames) the coder does not have a long term memory to assist with the excitation (often pitch), nor as just discussed, a predicted model for the filter. Thus the design of the LTP is somewhat critical to these hybrid coders.

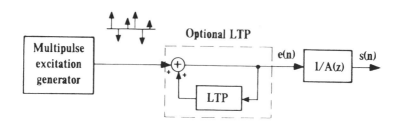

Figure 7.5 Outline of a multipulse excited linear predictive encoder

MPE-LPC coders provide near network quality speech (MOS = 4) at bit rates in the range of 16 to 8 kbps. Their performance deteriorates rapidly, however, at bit rates below 8 kbps. Acceptable performance can only be achieved by drastically modifying the basic multipulse excitation model.

A special case of MPE-LPC coding is the *regular-pulse excitation* (RPE) LPC coder which models the excitation signal with a sequence of equally spaced pulses. The performance of RPE systems is similar to that obtained from MPE coders. Various computationally efficient RPE schemes have been proposed and one of them has been chosen as the coding standard for the 'full-rate channel' of the GSM European mobile radio system. The codec operates at 13 kbps, a reasonably robust performance in the presence of channel errors, and can be implemented on a single DSP device. This performance does not come about for free, however. Speech path delay occurs and this attribute, or rather problem, is discussed further below.

The GSM speech coder is illustrated in its basic form in Figure 7.6. With an output rate of 13 kbps, the encoder processes 20 ms blocks of speech, and represents each block with 260 b. It is helpful to observe three functional parts of the encoder; namely, which perform the linear predictive analysis, long-term prediction, and excitation analysis, respectively. The linear predictor is an eight-tap filter characterized by eight log-area ratios, each represented by 3, 4, 5, or 6 b. In aggregate, the eight log-area ratios are represented by 36 b. Likewise, within the 20-ms block, the long-term predictor estimates pitch and gain four times (at 5 ms intervals). Each estimate produces a lag coefficient (7 b) and a gain coefficient (2 b). In total, the long-term predictor requires 36 b over the 20 ms frame. The remaining 188 b come from the regular pulse excitation analysis which, like the long-term predictor, operates over 5 ms sub-blocks, producing 47 b per sub-block, which adds up to 188 b.

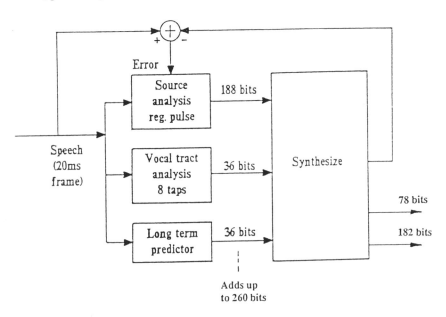

Figure 7.6 Regular-pulse excitation speech coder

For purposes of error protection, the speech coder has two categories of output bits in the total of 260 b. 182 'class 1' bits have a stronger influence on speech quality and are protected by three error-detecting parity bits and a half-rate convolutional code, so producing a sequence of 378 channel bits. As shown in Figure 7.7, this sequence is combined with the remaining 78 unprotected 'class 2' bits to form the 456 b speech signal. The aggregate bit rate of the speech signal, which was 182 + 78 (= 260 b), is now 456 b in 20 ms, = 22.8 kbps.

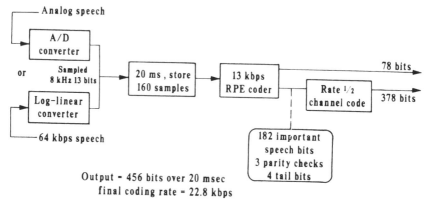

Figure 7.7 GSM source and channel coding

In a GSM receiver the 260 bits have to be unravelled out of the 456 b to operate the appropriate decode functions. The details are of course laid down in the full GSM specification, but are really too specific for full discussion here.

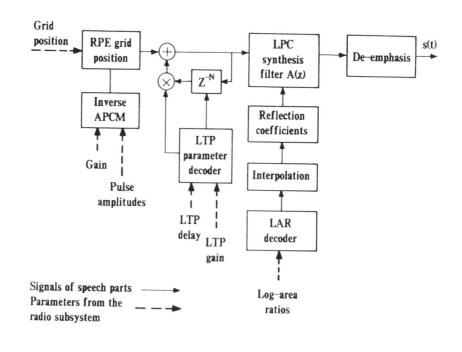

Figure 7.8 Outline of GSM-RELP digitized speech hardware decoding strategy

Figure 7.8 outlines the GSM RELP decoder and indicates the specific radio signal data bit allocation. Working from left to right, three pulse groups set up the appropriate RPE source, being synthesized directly from the low frequency tones of the original speech. Moving across, a further group of pulses control the LTP module. Finally, the bulk of the data is used to set up the parameters of the LPC synthesis filter, organized in a manner so as to require the least number of pulses (per speech segment). Pre-emphasis and de-emphasis are used in a manner similar for FM analog modulation systems.

7.3.4 Codebook vocoders

Continuous excitation linear predictive (CELP) coders employ a vocal tract LP-based model, or *codebook* based excitation model and an error criterion which serves to select an appropriate excitation sequence using an analysis-by-synthesis (AbS) optimization process. The system selects that excitation sequence which minimizes a perceptually weighted mean square error formed between the input and the locally decoded signals. The vocal tract model utilizes both a short-term filter (STF), which models the spectral envelope of speech, and a long-term filter (LTF), which accounts for pitch periodicity in voiced speech.

The main (fixed) excitation codebook was originally designed as a collection of random vectors (sequences), each of which is constructed using samples from a set of independent identically distributed Gaussian random variables having zero mean and unit variance. In this case the number of computations required to select the 'optimum' excitation sequence is prohibitively large and thus various simplified search strategies suitable for real-time implementation have been proposed. These codebook simplifications are based on efficient random codebooks, with a modelling performance that is equivalent to that of the Gaussian random codebook, but using structured and multistage codebook search strategies.

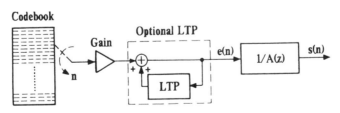

Figure 7.9 Outline of the CELP coder

An outline of a CELP coder is shown in Figure 7.9. Note the similarly to Figure 7.5, except that now the excitation is chosen from stored (codebook) models. More naturalness over and above RELP, or MPE-LPC, is possible for the same bit rate, or perhaps more importantly, a lower bit rate coder is allowable for operational performance.

In addition to the above modifications, whose aim is to improve computational efficiency, CELP speech quality can be enhanced by employing long-term filters with high temporal resolution and/or some form of post-filtering. CELP coders provide good toll quality speech at 8 kbps, with a typical MOS score of 3.7, while at 4.8 kbps CELP is far more successful than MPE-LPC in producing communication quality speech. The algorithm is now renamed as a *vector sum excited linear predictive* (VSELP), and is the one used as the 8 kbps North American standard for cellular telephony. The same algorithm has also been adopted at 6.7 kbps for the Japanese digital mobile radio system. The USA DoD (Department of Defense) 4.8 kbps speech coding standard is also a CELP-type system with speech quality comparable to 32 kbps CVSD speech.

The block diagram of the VSELP speech coder has the same form as Figure 7.6, i.e. the GSM coder, but the details of the excitation analysis and bit assignments differ and requires less bits, especially in the source analysis. With a source rate of 7.95 kbps, the North American code is more efficient than the 13 kbps code of GSM. The signal processing hardware of the coder is more complex, but with the developments in semiconductor technology it now pays to have an enhanced rate RELP encoder for GSM (known as ERC), based on the VSELP principles, and higher quality speech results for the same full rate coding rate of 13 kbps; see Figure 1.14, for example.

The VSELP coder likewise derives a new linear prediction every 20 ms. This linear predictor is characterized by ten log-area ratios, which are represented in aggregate by 38 b. The frame energy accounts for 5 b. The coder obtains long-term predictor coefficients at 5 ms intervals, four times per 20 ms block. The lag of each long-term predictor is represented by 7 b, accounting for 28 b per 20 ms block. As a form of codebook-excited linear prediction, the VSELP coder computes 14 b of excitation information in every 5 ms sub block. It also computes 8 b of gain information, which together represent a scaling factor for the long-term predictor and two scaling factors for the vector sum codebook. All this adds up to 159 b per 20 ms, or 7.95 kbps.

As in GSM, the output bits of the speech coder are divided into two categories, of which the 77 class 1 bits have a greater influence on speech quality than the 82 class 2 bits. The class 1 bits are protected by an error-detecting code and a half-rate convolutional code to produce a sequence of 178 channel bits, which are multiplexed with the 82 class 2 source bits to produce the 260 transmitted bits, as indicated in Figure 7.10. Two blocks of 260 b are interleaved and can be placed in the two assigned time slots of the 40 ms transmission frame of the D-AMPS system.

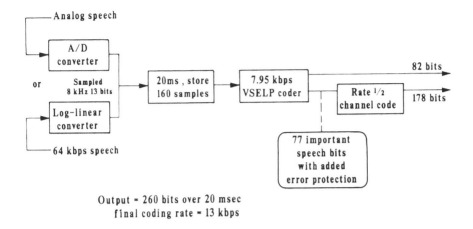

Output = 260 bits over 20 msec
final coding rate = 13 kbps

Figure 7.10 VSELP source and channel coding

7.4 Comparative performances

Table 7.1 Complexity and speech quality comparison for several speech coding techniques

Speech coding technique	Bit-rate kbps	Speech quality	Relative complexity	Algorith-mic delay (ms)
PCM (G711) (PSTN standard	64	toll	1	0.125
ADPCM (G721))	32	toll	10	0.125
CELP (G728)	16	toll	450	0.625
RELP (GSM standard)	13	communications	100	20
VSELP (US cellular standard)	7.95	communications	250	20
CELP (US DOD)	4.8	synthetic/comm-unications	400	45
IMBE (Skyphone) (Inmarsat typed M)	4.15	synthetic/comm-unications	150	28
LPC 10 (Military Standard)	2.4	synthetic	100	>23

The above description of speech coding strategies mainly focused on the obtainable speech quality (defined by the MOS) versus the channel data rate, a parameter of paramount interest to digital cellular radio design. There are two further penalties which must be observed. One is the group delay of the voice message through the chosen codec; the other is the hardware complexity which influences especially handset (MS) battery consumption and manufacturing costs (unless the consumer market becomes extraordinarily large, as it has done, and is doing for cellular). Table 7.1 sets out these facts for the principle speech coding systems. The PCM complexity is taken as the reference value.

The most serious column is the delay to the speech path as it is encoded and then decoded. The algorithmic delay (for GSM, say) is the 20 msec frame compulation, for example. Delay in a telephone system, whether it be mobile or fixed becomes unpleasant as it exceeds 100-200 msec. As the figures stand in Table 7.1 they seem acceptable; however, the figures must be doubled for any talker/listener path as well as adding any other signal delays.

Thus Table 7.2 sets out the forward path delay on a GSM (or D-AMPS) circuit, taking into account the various activities encountered on the way. It all adds up to 90 msec, much in part due to the interleaving activity described in Figure 1.24 and discussed again under multipath effects. This figure then doubles because of the return path, considering a duplex phone conversation.

Strategies for improving on this matter are being considered, as set out in the last two columns of Table 7.2. Essentially, shorter speech frames need be introduced and more robust radio paths (to reduce channel coding requirements). However, except under especially adverse situations, it is now well established that fully installed digital cellular systems provide a service, satisfactory to the MS users.

Table 7.2 Delay performance showing present and possible delay budget allocation

Source of delay	GSM delay, ms	Proposed delay ms	Improvement needed
Speech segmentation	20	2-5	lower delay coder
Speech encoding	3	1	faster signal processing
Digital link	17	6	broadband link
Switching	2	0.5	faster switching
Channel encoding	1	0.5	less channel coding
Interleaving	37	5-10	lower interleaving depth
Equalization	4	1	faster signal processing
Channel decoding	3	0.5	faster signal processing
Speech decoding	1	0.5	faster signal processing
Digital/analogue conversion	2	0.5-1	faster converters
Total	90	<30	

Further reading

Atal, B.S. (1982). 'Predictive coding of speech at low bit rates', *IEEE Trans Communications,* COM - 30, April, pp 600-614

Bellamy, J. (1990). *Digital Telephony*, Wiley, USA

Dimolitsas, S., Corcoran, F.L. and Baraniecki, M.R. (1994). 'Transmission quality of North American Cellular, Personal Communications, and Public Switched Telephone Networks', *IEEE Trans Veh Tech*, VT-43, May, pp 245-251

Flanagan, J.L. (1972). *Speech Analysis Synthesis and Perception*, Springer-Verlag, Heidelberg

Goodman, D.J. (1991). 'Second generation wireless information networks', *IEEE Trans Veh Tech,* VT-40, May, pp 366-374

Jayant, N.S. and Noll, P. (1984). *Digital Coding of Waveforms*, Prentice Hall, USA

Natvig, J.E. (1988). 'Evaluation of six medium bit-rate coders for the pan-European digital mobile radio system', *IEEE Journ. Select Area Comms,* 6, Feb, pp 324-331

Singhal, S., LeGall, D. and Chen, C.T. (1990). 'Source coding of speech and video signals', *Proc IEEE,* 78, July, pp 1233-1250

Wong, W.T.K. *et al* (1996). 'Low speech rate coding for telecommunications', *BT Technology Journ.*, January

Xydeas, C. (1991). Speech coding, in *Personal and Mobile Radio Systems,* Peter Peregrinus Ltd, UK

8 Multiple Access Strategies

8.1 Introduction

The purpose of this chapter is to discuss technologies which will allow a very large number of mobile radio subscribers to all have access to a limited amount of radio spectrum or frequency bands.

It is known that there is now a total of well over 40 million cellular telephone subscribers, growing at a rate of 40 per cent per year. At best, allowing 2×4 kHz radio bandwidth per subscriber (duplex conversation), this adds up to the *total* radio spectrum available below 1 GHz. Ignoring private mobile, paging and other services (and TV and radio), it is clear that cellular radio requires some imaginative access strategies in order to be accommodated in the allocated UHF bands centred around 900 MHz, and now 1800/1900 MHz.

The actual channel bandwidth per subscriber is, as has been described, closer to 2×25 kHz, but as we shall see, adjustment of this exact figure does not bear too strongly on multiple access principles.

8.2 Single subscriber aspirations

It is helpful to consider how any single subscriber views the activity. Confining the discussion to handportable operation, the subscriber's handset (MS) will generally operate in the conditions shown much earlier in Figure 1.6. The forward channel from the base station (BS) is heard by the receiver part; the reverse channel to the BS is generated by the transmitter section of the MS. The frequencies (centre of the signal spectrum bandwidth) used are dynamic, and hence the voltage controlled oscillator and synthesizer are another prerequisite, i.e., Figure 1.3.

The above generalization can be applied whether the system is analog or digital. In the case of digital systems, speech encoding and decoding strategies are applied before the voice signal comes from the microphone, or reaches the earpiece, respectively. An important difference is the level of semiconductor integration that can be employed in the handset by means of digital VLSI technology and this has been the enabling technology in present digital cellular radio. But this is transparent (hopefully) to our subscriber.

The part shown as memory and control also has a great bearing on the multiple access strategy, and we shall need to look at this in relation to the fixed network part of the cellular service.

Beforehand, however, we need to note the subscriber's number, which is now of the form: 03 + operator code + subscriber number. (Note that the number '3' could be changed by the telecommunications regulatory office.)

Outside the UK, the same phone can be reached on

00 + (country code) + 3 + etc.

This arrangement conforms to the CCITT E.164 numbering recommendation, shown earlier in Figure 1.26. Apart from the access digits (which are country dependent), the remaining numbers make up the *mobile station international ISDN number* (MSISDN).

This number can appear in phone directories and is of course known by the subscriber. We shall find later that the *public land mobile network* (PLMN) reached by this number, will often reconvert this number to a more secure number, known only by the controlling PLMN, called the *international mobile subscriber identification* (IMSI) number, which is used to signal over the network.

Moreover, the radio cell in which the subscriber is (temporarily) residing is also identified by a *cell global identification* (CGI) number. This number is made up of a set of numbers, i.e. the *location area identity* (LAI) and the *cell identity* (CI). The LAI is made up from the *mobile country code* (MCC), which identifies the (GSM) PLMN in the country being used, and a *location area code* (LAC) which identifies a group of cells in a PLMN. In other words, we have

CGI = MCC + MNC + LAC + CI

8.3 Multiple access strategy in a cell

Suppose we have 1 MHz of radio spectrum to allocate exclusively in each cell (actually 2×1 MHz for duplex operation).

The assured method is frequency division – leading to FDMA. Figure 3.1 showed FDMA using FM (or FSK) modulation.

25 kHz signalling would give 40 CH
12.5 kHz signalling would give 80 CH

AMPS (30 kHz) and TACS (25 kHz) use generous FDMA channels, the more so, since the FSK signalling tones at 10 and 8 kHz, respectively, can spill over into adjacent channels. Figure 8.1 shows the 'occupied bandwidth' in more detail, recalling the discussion on modulation.

NAMPS (10 kHz) and NMT (12.5 kHz) are very much more efficient, and also dispense with the above band audio signals and rely on baseband 200 and

1200 bps signalling. The narrowband TACS (NTACS) as used in Japan is similarly more efficient. With these systems, one is now looking at about 100 channels per MHz in 7-cell cluster cells.

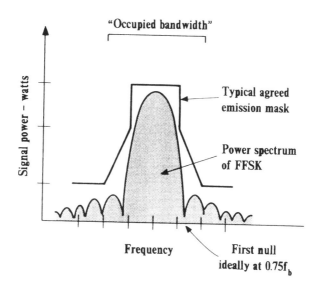

Figure 8.1 Transmitter emission characteristics

The problem with this approach is that FDMA limits the reuse principle, so much a part of cellular radio. The discussion in Chapter 3, section 4.2, shows clearly that one is unable to use the available frequencies in adjacent cells too soon, plus the fact that cell sizes cannot be made much smaller than about 0.5 km radius. This limits the spectral efficiency, described more fully in Chapter 10, which can really be stated as 'how many subscribers can be supported per square kilometre, or in a shopping centre for example'.

The number of subscribers that believe they are being offered individual service is, of course, rather larger than the number of individual radio channels because of the so-called trunking gain; see Figure 3.7. A more detailed discussion of this gain in Chapter 10 shows that a typical figure is about 30 times. Thus in Table 3.1, one finds that the number of subscribers per cell can rise considerably, only if the cluster size number N, can be reduced. On this score the established analog FDMA techniques are somewhat played out. The purpose of this chapter, as said, is therefore to introduce different access strategies.

8.4 Time division multiple access

An alternative way of using the available (allocated) spectrum is to let each user have access to the whole band for a short time (traffic burst), during which time he transmits his speech packet data much faster in the period allocated to him. He shares the frequency allocation with the other users who have time slot allocation at other times. Figure 8.2 shows a TDMA arrangement where the spectrum is only *partially* allocated, each user group A, B, C, D, having a time slot allocation in a particular channel group, 1, 2, 3, ...

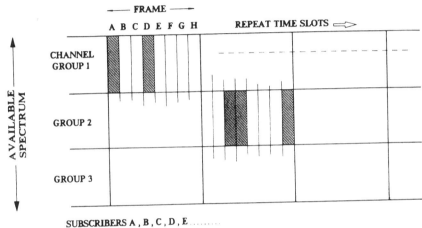

Figure 8.2 The TDMA mode of operation: each channel group of eight subscribers (A....H), send (and receive) messages as bursts. The number of base station transmitters is equal to the number of groups

This arrangement is sometimes known as *narrowband* TDMA. If all of the available spectrum (say, the forward channel – a similar picture will apply to the reverse channel) was allocated to each user during his time slot, this situation would be *wideband* TDMA. Each user would have to transmit data very rapidly, i.e. a high data rate, in order to pass traffic. Alternatively, more leisurely frames could be set up within the same channels, as apply to existing FDMA schemes. The ADC and JDC systems (defined below) intend to begin with just three time slots per frame. The relationship between the number of subscribers per group and frame length, etc., can be ascertained from Table 8.1.

Variation within the tabular data also occurs due to the speech coding rate assumed and the modulation efficiency. These two matters were discussed in the two preceding chapters.

For a chosen bit rate one could, as an exercise, calculate the various number of frames and frame length periods for various TDMA strategies. In practice, however, the systems being implemented are so tightly specified, plus the fact that many other factors in relation to the data within a frame have to be taken into consideration, that the exercise would be redundant.

Table 8.1 FDMA to TDMA changes

System	TACS	ADC	GSM
Multiple access	*FDMA*	*TDMA*	*TDMA*
Channels per carrier	1	3	8
Carrier spacing (kHz)	25	30	200
No. of carriers	400	333	50
No. of channels	400	999	400
Frame period (msec)	no limit	40	4.6
Channel data rate (kbps)	10	48	270

The table here assumes 10 MHz of spectrum available for each service in a frequency division duplex mode.

The breakdown of frames into time slots with the individual message content is shown in Figure 8.3. Several variations of this arrangement are possible.

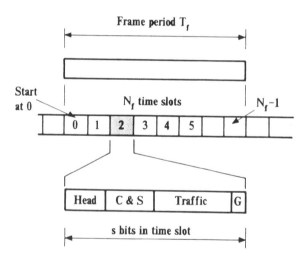

Figure 8.3 The frame, time slot and message relationship in TDMA

Here N_f channels per frame are shown. The convention is to start with number 0. Each time slot, belonging to an individual user, is made up of several parts, namely

Header message:	This contains carrier recovery; bit timing recovery; unique words; channel identity
C and S:	Control and signalling
Traffic:	This is the message part to the subscriber; typically; it would be encoded
G:	Guard space, to allow for time/distance delay, because of cell size

From Figure 8.3 it can be seen that much of the activity of a TDMA system is taken up with what is called identification and authentication. The overall bit rate allocated to each user is only a percentage of that available in a single-person-per-carrier scheme; on the other hand, no channels are uniquely allocated as control channels.

In TACS the control channels can be interpreted as reducing the spectral efficiency by 21/300 or 7%. Also, there is the difficulty of not being able to allocate alternate channels. In the TDMA schemes to be described, the efficiency will depend on the number of non-traffic bits.

8.4.1 Advantages of TDMA

What then are the advantages of TDMA to a cellular radio scheme?

* *Multiple circuits per carrier.* As indicated, all TDMA formats seek to multiplex at least two, and more often three, or eight, circuits per carrier. This represents lower investment at each base station site because of savings on transmitters and receivers (one pair per carrier, but N_f users).
* *Burst transmission.* The transmission from the mobile units is not continuous, but occurs during specified time slots only. This has many implications for circuit design and system control. It also impacts, positively, on the co-channel interference equation (3.2), since at any given moment only a percentage of the mobile units in operation are actually transmitting, leading to better frequency reuse (see Figure 3.13).
* *Bandwidth.* The bandwidths of current TDMA systems range from 25-30 kHz, equivalent to analog channels, to more than ten times this value. Bandwidth is determined in part by the choice of modulation technique and TDMA strategy; but to increase the efficiency, multi-level modulations have to be used. For a 270 kbps rate, for example, the symbol period is 3 µs, which is approximately the same as the delay spread that is expected in dense urban centres. Even using a higher level modulation to attain a modulation efficiency exceeding 2 bps/Hz would only increase the symbol time to 6 µs. Adaptive equalization is necessary. Some TDMA units may also be required to do slow-frequency hopping, to improve resistance to multipath fading. For TDMA systems with lower channel rates, however,

the equalization requirement may be no more severe than for FDMA systems.

- *Higher mobile-unit complexity.* The TDMA mobile unit has more to do than the FDMA entity, certainly on the digital-processing side, but with the continuing advances in VLSI circuitry, the added processing needed for TDMA appears to be no more than for analog phones.

- *Higher transmission overhead.* A TDMA slotted transmission forces the receiver to acquire synchronization on each burst; this is a fascinating procedure. Also, guard periods are necessary to separate one slot from another to allow for distant users. Because of this, TDMA systems need much more overhead than FDMA systems. The conventional view is that TDMA overhead requirements can run to more than 30% of the total bits transmitted. On the other hand, the measurement of path delay from frame to frame does allow more efficient handover procedures.

- *Lower shared-system costs.* As already indicated, the major advantage of TDMA systems over FDMA arises from the fact that each radio channel is effectively shared by a larger number of subscribers. The cost of the central-site equipment is significantly reduced.

- *No duplexers required.* An important advantage for TDMA over FDMA arises from the fact that by transmitting and receiving on different slots it is possible to eliminate the duplexer circuitry in the MS, replacing it with a fast-switching circuit to turn the transmitter and receiver on and off at the appropriate times.

- *Openness to technological change.* TDMA systems have another feature over FDMA, which outweighs everything else, at least to system designers and/or regulators who look to the long-term technological viability and flexibility of the system. As bit rates fall for speech coding algorithms, a TDMA channel is more easily reconfigurable to accept new techniques. Within the existing channel rate, the slot structure can be redefined to support lower bit rates or variable bit rates. A modification, if carried out with careful attention to other architectural constraints, could be implement-able by means of read-only memory (ROM) changes in the digital circuitry. Existing radio hardware can be utilized at the base station; also, a TDMA format can be designed to accommodate different time slot data structures, without disrupting the cellular network frequency plan.

- *Improved coverage.* Finally, as TDMA systems have been deployed, improved cell management techniques have been developed, such as hierarchical cell structures, which can fill in weak radio coverage areas, as well as give local capacity increases in both in-door and out-door centres.

8.4.2 TDMA systems worldwide

The following chapter describes major TDMA systems, but it is perhaps helpful to show the systems which have come into place, using TDMA, side-by-side. What is highlighted is the frame timing and the time slot structure, at least in the traffic (voice mode).

Thus Figure 8.4 shows the structure associated with the established *global system for mobile communications* (GSM). Originally developed for reserved bands around 900 MHz (see Figure 3.4), it can be used in general in Regions 1 and 3 of the world (Figure 1.9), and as a result, is almost a *de facto* standard throughout the world. In addition, wider frequency bands were reserved at 1800 MHz for foreseen *digital cellular systems* (DCS) and it was agreed that the same specification could be used as applies to GSM. Hence the DCS 1800 structure is the same as GSM, namely, Figure 8.4. Networks at 1.8 GHz are known as *personal communication networks* (PCN) and hence PCN networks conforming to the GSM specification will have the same radio interface structure as Figure 8.4.

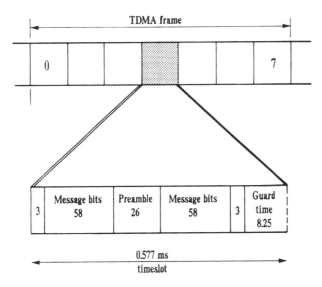

Figure 8.4 The GSM specified frame and time slot structure (in the voice/traffic mode)

In the USA, which also encompasses Region 2, the same frequency bands were (or are) not available. In order to have backward compatible TDMA networks to merge with the AMPS allocation (Figure 3.3), D-AMPS, often known as *American digital cellular* (ADC), has emerged as a standard (known as Interim Standard IS-54).

This has the structure shown in Figure 8.5. This is an even narrower band TDMA system (see also Table 8.1) partly forced on the standardization committee by the backward compatibility requirement. The same structure is being deployed in Japan where they have to fit in with their own 800 MHz allocations, and overlay their JTACS operations. The system is in this case known as *Japanese Digital Cellular* (JDC).

Another complication is the use of the words *personal communication services* (PCS). These are synonymous with PCN's, but due to the frequency availability one now has PCS 1900 bands. The nature of the air interface is not defined, but if a GSM system is deployed, one then has a PCS 1900 system, whose radio operation can be highlighted by Figure 8.4, i.e. the same as DCS 1800 or GSM 900. (The CDMA alternative is discussed below.)

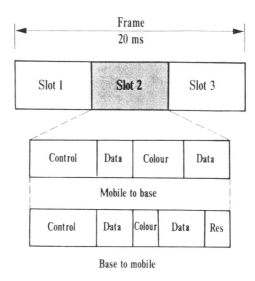

Figure 8.5 The D-AMPS frame and time slot structure
(See Chapter 9 Part 2 for a fuller description)

Because PCS can be regarded as a fixed network supporting feature, rather than a cellular network system as so far briefly outlined, it is important to mention two basic network attachments which make use of TDMA in the radio interface.

The first is the *digital European cordless telephone* (DECT). The TDMA frame and slot structure for one carrier, in the band 1880-1900 MHz, is shown in Figure 8.6. There are now twelve time slots per carrier, in other words a single BS could support 12 subscribers. The traffic information is now carried in one part of the time slot only. There are two parts to a frame since DECT is also a *time division duplex* (TDD) structure.

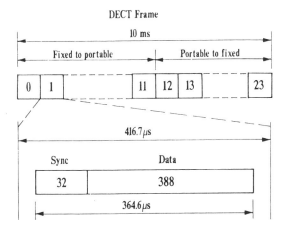

Figure 8.6 The DECT frame and time slot structure. There are 12 slots to a frame but a total of 24 because half are for the forward path, half for the reverse path, i.e. TDD operation

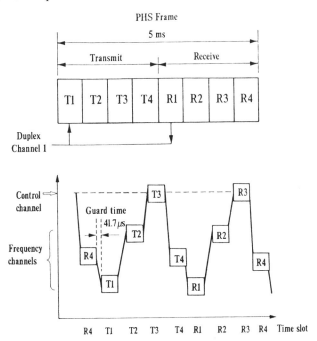

Figure 8.7 The PHS frame and time slot structure. There are 4 time slots to a frame, which become 8 because of TDD operation like DECT. Some time slots are used as dedicated control channels (unlike DECT, but like GSM) which subscribers lock to when idle

DECT can provide a higher data rate for a single user, by bundling time bursts together, or greater access to multiple users in a fixed conurbation, for example. Integrating DECT cordless capability within a wide-area cellular phone, such as NMT, is also being considered.

A competing system in another region is the Japanese *personal handyphone system* (PHS). The corresponding air interface structure is outlined in Figure 8.7.

8.5 Code division multiple access

In code division multiple access – CDMA, all the subscribers have access all the time to all of the frequency band. In order to be able to distinguish one signal from another, some form of code is employed such that each particular receiver will uniquely respond to his particular signal, which has his code. There are several ways of arranging the over-coding of the radio frequency signal which also has to carry the coded voice signal. These are discussed in subsequent sections.

8.5.1 Frequency-hopped spread-spectrum (FH/SS)

Here the baseband message is modulated on to a conventional channel, but now the signal is hopped (from channel to channel) under the control of a network specified *pseudo-random* (PN) code. The architecture outline is shown in Figure 8.8. The resulting spectrum appears to a casual listener to be a spread-spectrum signal. The processing gain can be shown to be equal to n, where n = number of frequency channels.

It is clear that the access gain of CDMA is not likely to exceed either an FDMA, or a TDMA strategy, if this was just the case.

What then could be the advantages of using FH/SS? Firstly, the signal of a particular user is unintelligible to a casual eavesdropper, even without any voice or data encryption. This was in fact why the technology was so well researched for military applications.

Secondly, FH guards against multipath fading and therefore the process of interleaving (and voice delay) can be avoided, see Figure 5.12.

For a cellular radio plan, and bearing in mind the importance of reuse and minimization of co-channel interference (as discussed in Chapter 10), it is clear that if the mobile allocated the *same* FH code in a reuse channel, but offset by one or more channel 'rest' intervals, it would now no longer interfere with the first cell. It is worth mentioning that handover under this protocol would not be a difficulty. Cells clusters could be reduced to N=3, (or even 1); and the access gain would rise by three or more times (according to Table 3.1). This is for the same allocated bandwidth and n channels.

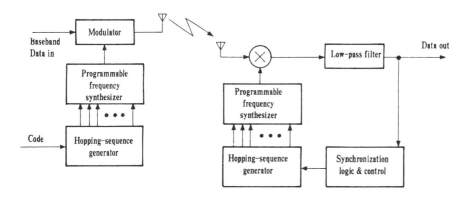

Figure 8.8 Outline schematic of a FH/SS send and receive system

One matter which would need attention, however, is the linearity of the MS receiver. The wanted signal could be from (or to) the limit of a cell, whilst another MS could be close by and hopping past at full power. Acquiring synchronization is not without difficulties either.

8.5.2 Direct-sequence spread-spectrum (DS/SS)

Here a full channel pseudo-random code spreading signal is multiplexed on to the voice data and spreads the transmitted RF spectrum over the available bandwidth, indicated in Figure 8.9.

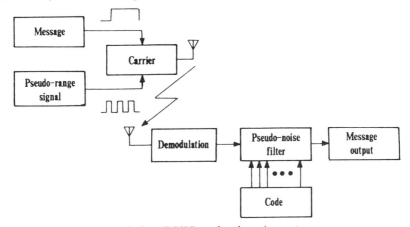

Figure 8.9 Outline schematic for a DS/SS send and receive system

The processing gain, for a code matched receiver is

$$G_p = \frac{BW_{RF}}{R_{message}} = \frac{2 \times R_c}{R_b}$$

where R_c = PN code rate, and R_b = data bit rate

This gain has to be such that the SNR at the receiver output exceed some threshold, such as 10 dB, above all other signals being likewise modulated, but using other PN sequences.

A brief note of PN sequences may be helpful here. They are readily generated by a series of shift registers; an example of three stages, which will generate a 7b PN sequence, is shown in Figure 8.10(a). The output sequence when modulo-2 added to the same sequence produces a very strong autocorrelation output, is shown in Figure 8.10(b); i.e. only the same PN sequence produces a recognizable output. As the number of shift register stages n is increased, the *maximum length* of the output PN sequence becomes equal to $2^n - 1$.

For example if:

	sequence length
n = 3	= 7
n = 8	= 255
n = 16	= 65,535
n = 20	≥ 1 million

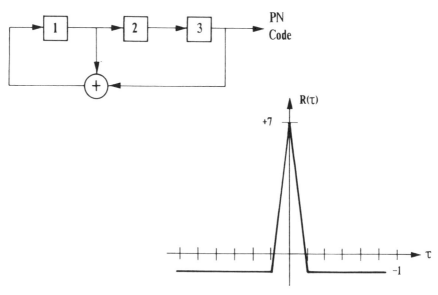

Figure 8.10   A three-stage shift register generating a 7b sequence and its auto-correlation response

This illustrates the power of such sequences. An example of their application is in the synchronization burst channel (SCH) in GSM, referred to in section 9.2.8.

The modulator used in the DS/SS system, Figure 8.9, is usually considered to be a BPSK modulator, as shown in Figure 6.6. The input to the modulator is now the sum of the higher rate PN code and the slower rate traffic data, e.g. see Figure 8.11. The signal spectrum will have a $\sin x/x$ shape, with the first null determined by the PN code rate (called the chip rate). Since the signal is allocated a wideband spectrum; for example 1.25 MHz as specified in the US CDMA standard IS-95, the realization of a channel filter of the order of 1 MHz for both MS transmitter and receiver is not a difficult task. More usually QPSK is employed (see Figure 6.12) so the filter would be the bandpass filter depicted in the diagram.

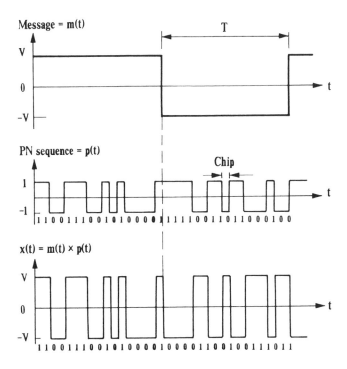

Figure 8.11 The two digital signal streams associated with a DS/SS system

A sketch of a CDMA DS/SS spectrum is shown in Figure 8.12. The PN sequence rate used is 1.2288 MHz, and the user data rate is 19.2 kHz. The spectrum is continuous in the band because of the randomness of the chip timing (Figure 8.11).

Cellular Radio

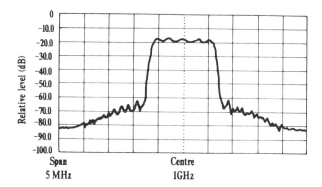

Figure 8.12 The RF spectrum typical of a CDMA DS/SS system, here centred at 1 GHz

All users would generate the same looking spectrum across the allocated band. It is only when this signal is demodulated (multiplied) by the correct (same) PN sequence that an output equal to the message data appears. To other users the DS/SS signal (Figure 8.11) appears as noise in the receiver wideband front end, above the usual site and receiver noise figure noise. Setting aside the problem of acquiring synchronization between the MS and BS, and during handover, this CDMA strategy appears to offer a very large individual access opportunity, and excellent cell reuse potential.

There is, however, a difficulty, as with most schemes. This is what is known as the *near–far* effect. The above discussion assumed that the signals received by one base station were of the same power. This can be the case for a space satellite system, but on the ground the signal level, as we saw earlier, changes very rapidly with distance, especially as one comes close to a BS, for example. The processing gain equation will no longer be true. To restore matters, a very strict power control algorithm must be put in place, which is not an easy task in a multi-user cellular environment. Details on these strategies can be found in the references cited. The principles are clear enough, but assured practical operation appears to be just over the horizon.

An interesting feature of the DS/SS is that the signal reaching a mobile is continuous, once synchronization has been acquired. As a result very good voice quality can be achieved, especially with the enhanced rate voice coders working at 13 kbps. There are no interleaving problems and perhaps fewer missed bits, together with the opportunity for *seamless* handover. Users are now very sensitive to the grade-of-service (voice quality) of a cellular service. What perhaps needs to be established is the time to acquire synchronization with the network if a dense user scenario comes about.

8.5.3 Coded orthogonal frequency division modulation (COFDM)

To return again to the matter of service, all participants are striving for quality of service, e.g. no dropped calls, excellent voice quality and gapless coverage. The last two multiplexing schemes were more than interesting in the sense that they both provided protection against multipath fading, due to their inherent frequency diversity attribute. At the same time, they assume that a very large amount of digital signal processing can be built into the MS, for example, without requiring undue power consumption (acceptable battery life).

Radio and TV broadcasters are equally interested in digital technology, and have proposed a form of modulation, which falls between the above two CDMA proposals, and is interesting to describe briefly as the type of technology that may be developed for cellular radio in future schemes.

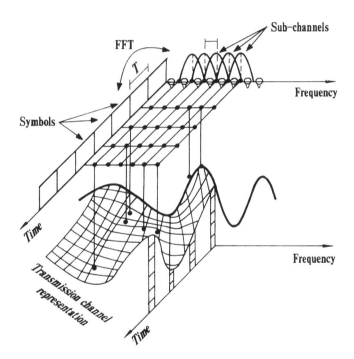

Figure 8.13 Two-dimensional representation of COFDM

The modulation is called COFDM on account of the fact that the message data is divided up between a large number of closely spaced carriers, with only parts of the whole message being sent on each carrier. At the same time, the individual carrier messages are under the umbrella of common convolutional coding. Thus, in effect one has a FH system multiplexed with an SS code. By this means, errors on any one carrier due to multipath fading are naturally corrected, and very acceptable BER rates are achieved once the signal exceeds an E_b/N_o ratio greater than, say, 10 dB. The individual carriers can be more closely spaced than the individual symbol rate on each carrier by choosing them to be orthogonal. In this way, their individual sidebands can overlap without producing interference on the adjacent carriers.

A schematic representation of COFDM is shown in Figure 8.13. To map the symbols (on each carrier) on to the spectrum, a *fast Fourier transform* (FFT) technique must be employed. This is where the remarks made earlier concerning the need for additional processing power come to the fore. It is worth noting that modulation efficiencies of 0.8 b/Hz have been quoted, which is just half that of $\pi/4$ DQPSK.

Further reading

Dixon, R.C. (1984). *Spread Spectrum Systems*, Wiley Interscience, USA

Elbert, B.R. (1996). 'Future satellite mobile telephone networks', Chapter 13 in *Modern Personal Radio Systems*, IEE Press, London

Gardiner, J. and West, B. (Eds) (1995), *Personal Communication Systems and Technologies*, Artech House, Boston and London

Kohno, R., Meidam, R., and Milstein, L.B. (1995). 'Spread spectrum access methods for wireless communications', *IEEE Communications Magazine*, January, pp 58-67

Maral, G. and Bousquet, M. (1986). *Satellite Communication Systems*, John Wiley, Chichester

Pommier, D. and Ratliff, P.A. (1988). 'High quality digital sound broadcasting to mobile, portable and fixed receivers', *IEE International Broadcasting Conference*, 293 , September

Pommier, D. (1993). 'Description and features of the COFDM system', *IEE Colloquium on Terrestrial DAB*, London, February 17

Rappaport, T.S. (1996). *Wireless Communications; Principles and Practice*, IEEE Press, NY

Steele, R. (1994). 'The Evolution of Personnel Communications', *IEEE Personal Communications*, October, pp 6-11

Tsui, T.S.D. and Clarkson, T.G. (1994). 'Spread-spectrum communication techniques', *IEE Elec Comms J*, February, pp 3-12

9 Digital Cellular Designs

9.1 Second generation networks

Analog cellular is known as a first generation wireless information telephone network. There are up to six incompatible analog cellular standards world-wide, even though they have the underlying FM FDMA mode of operation. The main aim of the so-called second generation systems was (i) to go digital, (ii) to have a single standard. The first has taken place; but the second has not been achieved. The mode of operation will feature *time division multiple access* (TDMA), but matters like frame timing, method of modulation and error-correction code procedures differ from one global system to another. The three main systems in use at present are:

- GSM   Global system for mobile communications ; which also includes DCS 1800/PCS 1900
- ADC   American digital cellular: called D-AMPS. An alternative candidate is CDMA
- JDC   Japanese digital cellular: PHS can also be associated here

We will, therefore, divide this chapter into three parts. The first part we head *European digital cellular designs*; and work down the above list, keeping the chapter sections in numerical order, however. Because several designs have several similar features, the later parts of the chapter will become smaller, since repetition of such features would hardly add value to the text.

These second generation systems have reached a highly advanced state of design. The principles and design can therefore be described with some accuracy. Again, the availability of the radio spectrum (by allocation) has dictated the way in which the systems have come about and the TDMA frame arrangements were briefly described in the previous chapter.

Third generation systems are also being researched, especially using methods such as code division multiple access and controlled packet allocation. The details of methods therein, at present, are somewhat outside the scope of this text and fully agreed designs are not universally available. Also, a problem for these systems may be the fact that the second generation systems, to be described, are now so well entrenched, as well as a desire to see a return on their investment costs, that when all these factors are added together, plus the forthcoming mobile satellite service investment plans, they could be difficult to justify in all situations.

Part 1: European digital cellular designs

9.2 GSM

In TDMA, as described, each user has access to the band for a short time (traffic burst), during which time he transmits data much faster. He shares his frequency allocation with the other users who have time slot allocation at other times. Figure 8.2 showed a *narrowband* TDMA arrangement where the spectrum is *partially* allocated, i.e. each user group A, B, C, D, ..., having a time slot allocation in a particular channel group, 1, 2, 3. These radio channels are again marked by their centre frequency, called the *absolute radio frequency channel number* (ARFCN).

The frequencies allocated to GSM are:

Downlink   (925) 930 to 960 MHz
Uplink   (880) 890 to 915 MHz

This spectrum allocation at 900 MHz is categorized into a *primary* GSM band and the *extended* GSM band. Both bands support full duplex transmission using two sub-bands spaced 45 MHz apart. The standard, or primary, GSM band runs from 890 MHz to 915 MHz on the uplink (mobile transmits, base receives), and 935 MHz to 960 MHz (base transmits, mobile receives) on the downlink. The extended GSM band runs from 880 MHz to 915 MHz on the uplink and 925 MHz to 960 MHz on the downlink.

In countries where analog TACS systems exist, the primary GSM band may be subdivided further into a TACS sub-band and a GSM sub-band. The former occupies the lower 15 MHz of the 25 MHz duplex allocation, while the latter occupies the upper 10 MHz duplex band. For the primary GSM band, the radio frequency channels (ARFCN) are numbered from 1 to 124; the corresponding frequency can be found from the following equations:

Mobile transmits $F_{up}(n) = 890.2 + 0.2 (n - 1)$ MHz
Base transmits $F_{down}(n) = F_{up}(n) + 45$ MHz

For the DCS 1800 band, the frequency band runs from 1710 MHz to 1785 MHz on the up-link, and 1805 MHz to 1880 MHz on the down-link. Full duplex transmission is supported by using two sub-bands spaced 96 MHz apart. Similar to the primary GSM band, the radio frequency channels for the DCS1800 band are numbered from 512 to 885 and the corresponding frequency can be found from the following equations:

Mobile transmits $F_{up}(n) = 1710.2 + 0.2\,(n - 512)$ MHz
Base transmits $F_{down}(n) = F_{up}(n) + 95$ MHz

With a guard band of 200 kHz at each end of the sub-bands and the radio frequency channel spacing of 200 kHz, a maximum of 174 carriers is thus allowed in the extending GSM band and 374 carriers in the DCS 1800 band.

For a start up GSM network, a minimum of 12 carriers is normally required. For satisfactory quality of service, however, most regulators allocate 24 or more carriers to an operator, so that two carriers can be implemented within each cell, giving about fifteen traffic channels per cell.

The pan-European cellular mobile radio system was conceived in 1982 by a committee of the *Conference of European Posts and Telecommunications Administrations* (CEPT). They foresaw a need for public cellular radio, but not accompanied by a widening divergence of systems, especially as was the case for analog, so a standard was gradually put in place to positively encourage convergence. It also wished to achieve a measure of compatibility with ISDN. The system that emerged from this process is the GSM system. GSM stands for *global system for mobile communications;* previously it was named after the planning group shown in Figure 9.1. In 1989 this technical committee was transferred from CEPT to the *European Telecommunications Standards Institute* (ETSI).

ETSI is a legal entity. It has over 300 members among the industrial community as well as the telecommunications operators and a large permanent staff located in purpose-built accommodation near Nice, in the south of France. It deals with a wide range of telecommunication standardization matters through a General Assembly and a Technical Assembly which meet several times a year; the relevant part of the structure of ETSI is shown in Figure 9.1.

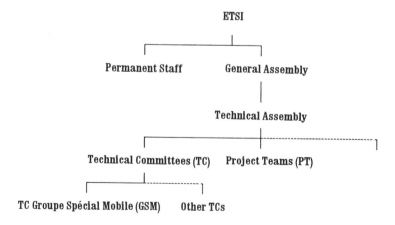

Figure 9.1 Outline structure of ETSI. The GSM technical committee was known as the Special Mobile Group

9.2.1 Features of GSM

The primary function of GSM is to provide a full roaming mobile telephony service, by means of a mobile cellular network.

The services provided by the GSM system are recognized as falling into three categories:

- teleservices,
- bearer services,
- supplementary services

The following description refers to the so-called *Phase One* of GSM. The offerings of *Phase Two* are listed in Appendix 2.

The term *teleservice* refers to those services provided on a user-terminal to user-terminal basis. The most important teleservice is clearly voice communication. Facsimile transmission also belongs to this category. Another example is the short message service (rather like alphanumeric paging) in which a message received by a mobile can be read directly from the built-in display.

In *bearer services* the terminal equipment is provided by the user, the responsibility of the network-service provider ending at the point of connection. Many forms of data transmission, at rates between 300 and 9600 bps, fall into this category. GSM provides no specific error protection for so-called transparent data links: in such situations the user must provide any necessary protection. In non-transparent data services, a GSM radiolink protocol will protect the data, but at the same time reduce the maximum data rate to 4800 bps. However, improved rates are being developed.

Supplementary services are being developed along the lines of planned ISDN services, but are likely to vary greatly from country to country. Among the first to be introduced will be call forwarding, advice of charge, call barring and conference facilities.

With GSM, subscription is recorded in a subscriber card or 'smart card'. This *subscriber interface module* (SIM) is part and parcel of the complete GSM network. These cards are like a normal size credit card (or it may be a much smaller card for use in hand-held phones), but contain a complete microcomputer with memory. Therefore, these cards can perform many functions and also provide a high level of security. As a brief starting outline, when such a card is plugged into a GSM phone it assigns the MIN code; it also checks that the subscription is valid, and the card not stolen, by authenticating the call back to the user's home database.

This provides exceptional security, preventing false charges to the user's account and ensures that incoming calls are correctly delivered. Other useful and novel features include the ability to store user information, such as a list of short codes for dialling frequently used numbers. Voice security is also greatly enhanced by the use of full digital encryption. This applies equally for voice and for data calls.

Speech quality on GSM now equals analog systems under average to good conditions. However, under conditions of a weak signal or bad interference, GSM can perform significantly better, and the network roll-out plans have quality of service as a prime considering, as will become evident later.

The data services can offer a performance with low errors, which will also become faster and more diversified with time.

Size, weight and battery life are important parameters of handset performance. With the digital circuitry employed, and the exceptionally high level of silicon implementation now available, smaller, lighter and long duty life phones are now available and expected.

The GSM standard is an *open standard* in the form of recommendations. They fill some 5000 pages and now more, divided into the following main sections:

    0   Preamble
    1   General vocabulary, abbreviations
    2   Service aspects
    3   Network
    4   MS-BS interface and protocols
    5   Physical layer on radio path
    6   Audio aspects
    7   Terminal adapters for mobiles
    8   BTS/BSC and BSC/MSC interfaces
    9   Network interworking
    10 Service interworking
    11 Network management, operations and maintenance
    12 Equipment specifications and type-approval

Clearly, the recommendations occupy a much greater area of paper than this book, or indeed many other books; however, because we are concentrating mainly on the cellular *radio* aspects, the critical recommendations can be summarized, by focusing on numbers 4 and 5 in particular.

9.2.2 *The OSI reference model*

A system of the complexity of GSM, or indeed any of the other competing digital cellular networks, requires much planning and organization, both in the definition and in its practical implementation. A pattern for structuring data communication networks in general has been provided by the *International Standards Organization* (ISO) in the form of the *open systems interconnection* (OSI) model. The OSI model provides for a number of horizontal layers, each layer communicating exclusively, and according to well-defined rules, with the layers immediately above and below it. Communication thus becomes vertical, rather than horizontal, except for the lowest, or physical layer, where the information is passed from one system to the other. The GSM specifications or recommendations as listed above have been written to fully define the lower three layers of this OSI model, see Table 9.1.

Table 9.1 OSI model and the use of three lowest layers (1 to 3) in GSM

OSI Layer Number	OSI Layer Name	GSM Equivalent Model	Tasks
7	Application	-	User tasks
6	Presentation	-	
5	Session	-	Network tasks
4	Transport	-	
3	Network	Call management Mobility management Radio resources	
2	Data link	Concentration Segmentation Acknowledgement	GSM network tasks
1	Physical	Error detection Channel coding Modulation	

- In the lowest layer, layer 1, the *physical* characteristics of the transmission or radio path medium are specified. In the context of the GSM radio link, this definition includes not only the frequencies, modulation types, etc., but also the structure of the bursts and frames implicit in a time division multiplex transmission scheme. Since this layer is responsible for the correct transmission of single bits, an element of error-protection coding also belongs here.

- Layer 2, or the data-link layer, consists of an intelligent entity responsible for the safe communication of meaningful messages or frames between radio stations. To this end the transmitting section structures the messages of the higher layer to match the physical constraints of the layer 1 medium and requests, in many situations, a confirmation (acknowledgement) from the receiving end. At the receiving end messages are reconstructed from the received frames and the acknowledgements are formulated for retransmission.

- Layer 3, the network layer, is responsible for management of all calling and related activity of the radio network. These tasks are further subdivided into sub-layers designated call control management, mobility management and radio resource management.

- The higher layers apply to any telecommunications system and specific reference to these tasks does not appear in the table of GSM recommendations, listed in section 9.2.1.

Figure 9.2 shows how the OSI rules change the MS operation into vertical communication layers, as opposed to the usual horizontal serial operation.

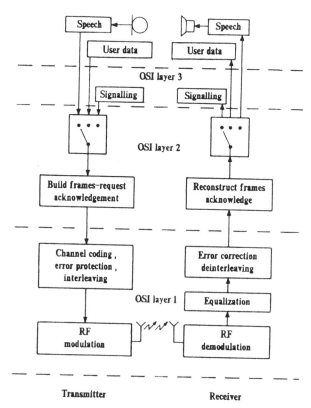

Figure 9.2 An OSI model for the mobile part, showing the first three layers

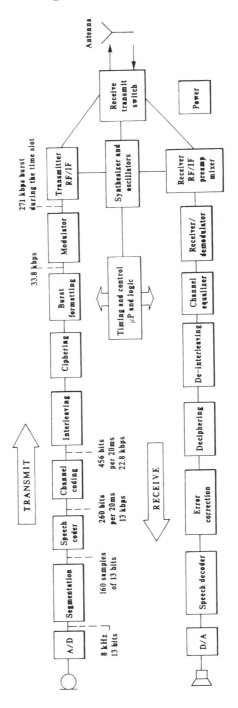

Figure 9.3 Functional block diagram of a GSM digital cellular mobile station

In Figure 9.3 the same 'phone' is drawn in a conventional manner. (This diagram should be compared to Figure 1.3.) The receive/transmit frequencies are similar, as could be the front-end circuits, except that digital cellular works in a burst mode. The back-end of the MS differs considerably, however, because of the extensive digitization and control needed.

The detailed operation of the parts, or functions, within the MS as set out in these two diagrams will become clearer once the radio interface aspect of the GSM operation is explained in the following sections, but since the MS forms a specific entity within the GSM mobile cellular network, some account of the network is useful before one launches further into the system.

9.2.3 *The fixed network supporting GSM*

When the GSM committee started its work much of the effort was concentrated on the radio system. This reflected the essential, and what was initially viewed as the main difference between a mobile network and a fixed public switched telecommunication network (PSTN); that is, the substitution of the subscriber's local loop by a mobile radio path. It was therefore appropriate that attention was focused on the radio aspects. However, the mobile cellular network (which can be called a PLMN) has brought new dimensions into public communications, so the network aspects of the system need to be considered early on.

First of all, the fixed network is not unlike other networks supporting cellular; in fact, Figure 1.8 is very applicable to GSM. However, within this architecture the interfaces can be defined as set out in Figure 9.4. This is a diagram similar to Figure 1.8, but is drawn to emphasize *interfaces.*

There are several interfaces; they are all important for the operation of the system, but only those relating to the radio and network access are discussed in any detail here. Other interfaces include, for example, the *subscribers interface module* (SIM), which personalizes a mobile station. Some MSs will have a slide-in, smart-card SIM and some a wired-in one that is not user-changeable.

Two mandatory interfaces are (i) the A-interface which connects a *base station system* (BSS) to the MSC, and (ii) the Um, or air interface, which provides the connection of the BS to the antenna, and hence MSs. Within the BSS part there is the *base station controller* (BSC) and the *base transceiver station* (BTS). Here the PSTN PCM digital speech can be converted to GSM RELP coded speech and vice versa.

This unit is known as a *transcoder* (TRAU) and converts the encoded speech from the 20 msec 16 kbps blocks into 64 kbps telephony PCM. TRAUs may be found in three places, as indicated in Figure 9.5. This actually indicates that the A-bis is only loosely defined. Nowadays, the transcoder units are usually associated with the main, or mobile switching centre.

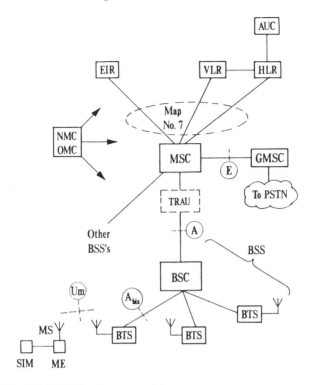

Figure 9.4 The GSM PLMN reference model

Referring to Figure 9.4 (or Figure 1.8, or indeed Figure 3.20, which described analog cellular), we note that a GSM network has all the entities, which have been defined earlier in the book, but it is useful to repeat for the description to follow. Thus the main entities are:

- SIM   -   subscriber interface module (card)
- MS   -   mobile station (Rx/Tx part)
- BTS   -   base transreceiver part (one serving up to eight MS because of TDMA format)
- BSC   -   base station(s) controller
- BSS   -   base station system., = BTS + BSS
- MSC   -   mobile (services) switching centre
- GMSC   -   gateway management switching centre
- HLR   -   home locating registrar
- VLR   -   visitor locating register
- AUC   -   authentication centre
- EIR   -   equipment identity register
- OMC   -   operations and management centre
- NMC   -   network management centre

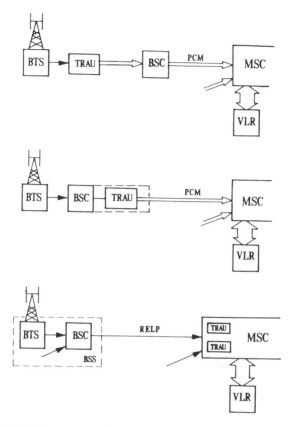

9.5 Positions for the transcoder unit in a GSM network

GSM will have at least one home location register (HLR), where all management data relating to all home MSs is stored, and at least one visitor location register (VLR), where selected data relating to visiting MS's is stored. This data includes the *international mobile station identity* (IMSI), the MS international ISDN number, and other information, including the current location of the MS. The HLR and a VLR will be co-located with the *anchor* mobile services switching centre (MSC).The number of subsidiary VLRs will depend on the size of the network. Thus the interfaces between the MSC, the HLR and the VLR must also be defined, as indicated in Figure 9.4. One exception is the *gateway MSC* (GMSC) whose purpose is to accept incoming, and outgoing, PSTN calls and route them specifically, but a VLR is not needed for this purpose. MAP stands for the communication protocol between the network subsystem elements and is known as the *mobile application part* of GSM; signalling system No. 7 is known as the *telephone user part*.

For a cellular system to track a mobile requires data registers that store the location and characteristics of the mobile. In terms of a GSM network, the ultimate store of such information is the HLR, which is effectively the central subscriber database. In a simple system it would be accessed every time the mobile has to communicate. This is impractical in a worldwide system where the signalling load requirements to exchange information with the HLR would be significant. Hence GSM also defines VLRs, which provide a very efficient mechanism to distribute the 'load'. VLRs retain all the necessary information for authenticating and servicing a mobile area and are used to handle the initial signalling and routing information for the mobile. The accessing of the HLR is therefore reduced to the identification of the VLR and the updating of the data stored in the VLR, which temporarily holds the subscriber details. Once a VLR has successfully recorded the details the procedures of routing, verification and authentication are handled by it. Meanwhile, the HLR is a fault tolerant database, often situated at the operator's central administration centre (NMC/-OMC) and holds semipermanent and transient data.

The semipermanent data record would contain the following:

- mobile/subscriber's identity numbers
- services/capability
- restrictions

Transient data is related to mobility and is updated by means of signalling procedures with the VLR. The main elements of transient data are:

- address of the last known VLR that served the mobile
- address of the subscriber data in the VLR database
- subscriber's restrictions relating to the relevant network

The VLR is often implemented within the MSC framework, but is a separate entity. This implementation is chosen for convenience and cost effectiveness. It is also possible to realize the VLR to be physically similar to the HLR. The VLR contains more precise location information and is updated every time there is a location update of the mobile.

A structured procedure, e.g. call set up, location update or handover, involves interaction between most of the network entities, with protocols defined in the specifications. As an example, when a mobile originated call is made, the MS first accesses the BTS to request a dedicated resource on the radio interface. If the call request is accepted the BTS grants a channel and the signalling between the MS and the network can commence. During that process the MS is authenticated by checking the identity of the subscriber and the identity of the equipment against the stored information in the AUC. This process is expedited by using the VLR, which tends to be more local to a roaming subscriber. Call data is logged at the OMC, along with other performance and alarm information from the network entities, so that the operator always has a reliable assessment of the network.

Among the selected data transferred from the HLR to the VLR will be the services available to that MS, for example, supplementary voice services or data services. At the time of initiating a call, specific details of the services requested will be required from the MS. It can be seen that the signalling activity on both the radio path and on the fixed links of the system is considerable. In fact, emulation and experience of digital cellular networks shows that the utilization rate of the HLR to VLR path increases faster than any other link in the overall network and this rate may limit the dimensioning of an installed network.

The international signalling system CCITT No. 7, as used by the fixed telephone services, has been specified for the network management and interconnection signalling functions of the GSM system; the requisite mobile application part is in fact one of the largest of the GSM recommendations and runs to over 600 pages. This illustrates the level to which GSM standardization has been implemented by the ETSI GSM technical committee.

9.2.4 The radio part

The radio part is known as the *radio resource* (RR) in GSM and comprises the various aspects of the interface between base stations and mobile stations – the mobile radio link. Also called the *air interface*, it includes the definitions of the logical, i.e. the traffic and control channels; the physical channels, i.e. the radio frequencies and time slots and their make up, the multiple access, multiplexing, frequency hopping, coding and interleaving, modulation, power control and handover, synchronization, transmission and reception.

Also included are the specifications of spurious emissions which could potentially have an adverse effect on other services. These arise from the modulation process and the power ramping at the beginning and end of each time slot, as discussed below, as well as the usual imperfections in the actual implementation of the oscillator, frequency synthesizer and other radio frequency elements that make up a mobile radio station.

All the physical (layer 1) radio aspects are covered in the RR recommendations and are accommodated within fewer than 200 pages, whereas the layer 3 functions relating to the MS-BS interface require many hundreds of pages for their full specification.

As with the first generation TACS network, several classes of mobile are assumed. The trend today is to only use handportables. They will perform excellently in the small cells that typify dense urban and city areas and where there will be much greater numbers of users. In such city areas with a large number of small cells the maximum BS power output is unlikely to be necessary, and while this may not balance the path loss, it ensures that handheld MSs are used well within their capabilities in most cases. The exception to this is the use of hand-held MSs inside buildings, lifts, underground railway stations and other locations where radio penetration from a conventional mast top BS antenna is weakened, as discussed in Chapter 2. More on this subject, however, is left until Chapter 10.

Table 9.2 lists the peak mobile power allowable performance of the various GSM/DCS1800 MS units. The minimum power is usually +13 dBm.

Table 9.2 Power classes of the GSM 900 and DCS 1800 MS units

Class	GSM 900	DCS1800
Mobile TX peak power (maximum)		
Class 1	20W (+43 dBm)	1W (+30 dBm)
Class 2	8W (+39 dBm)	0.25W (+24 dBm)
Class 3	5W (+37 dBm)	
Class 4	2W (+33 dBm)	
Class 5	0.8W (+29 dBm)	
Mobile TX peak power (minimum)		
Class 1	+13 dBM	+10 dBm
Class 2	+13 dBM	+4 dBm
Class 3-5	+13 dBM	
RX sensitivity (portable phone)	−102 dBm	−100 dBm

Table 9.3 summarizes several of the parameters of the air interface. In the context of the discussion here, two critical parameters affect the R_X/T_X spacing. In frequency, it is 45 MHz (as is the case for TACS); in time, it is three time slots. Thus, in Figure 9.3 the reverse channel is operating three time slots later.

Table 9.3 GSM air-interface parameters

Mobile to BS	890-915 MHz
BS to mobile	935-960 MHz
Channel spacing	200 kHz
R_X/T_X spacing - frequency	45 MHz
R_X/T_X spacing - time	1.15 ms
Modulation	0.3 GMSK
Users per frequency pair	8
Frame period	4.615 ms
Time slot period	576.9 µs
Bit period	3.692 µs
Bits per time slot	148
Transmission rate	270.833 kbps

A good way of illustrating the radio paths involved is shown in Figure 9.6. One BS is assigned to one radio frequency in a channel group, but can communicate to eight MSs since there are 8 time slots, see Figure 8.2. Meanwhile, the MS has to switch from R_X to T_X in about one msec (2 time slots), but more time is allowed for T_X to R_X operation. Other units will be operating in other channels or time slots

To give some idea of the requirements made on the RF circuit design by the GSM specification, Figure 9.7 shows the switching time of a device changing the radio channel from 890 to 935 MHz, here within 400 μs, i.e. one-third of the timing period specified.

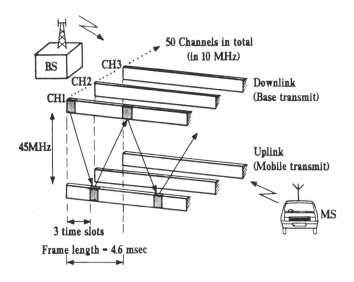

Figure 9.6 RF activity between a base station and a mobile

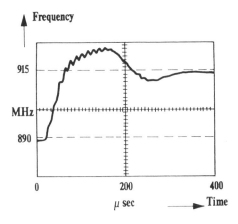

Figure 9.7 A phase locked loop synthesizer changing frequency by 25 MHz at 900 Mhz

9.2.5 The timing structure of GSM

The most prominent characteristic of the GSM physical layer is the elaborate timing structure. GSM carriers are spaced at 200 kHz intervals, each carrying a 270.833 kbps digital signal. To organize the information transmitted on each carrier, GSM defines several time intervals, ranging from 0.9 μs (*one-quarter bit*) to 3 h 28 m 53.760 s (*cryptographic hyperframe*).

Terminals and base stations insert information into the channel in *time slots*, each of duration 577 μs. Eight consecutive time slots comprise a TDMA *frame* of duration 4.62 ms, while 26 frames comprise a *multiframe* with duration 120 ms. Figure 8.3 introduced the arrangement of a time slot in a frame, now to be seen in the lower part of the diagram of Figure 9.8. Note how the multiframes can be transposed, since there are two extra frames in a set of frames having eight time slots. These are for the purpose of non-traffic time slots burst transmission. There is a whole heirarchy of control and signalling opportunities within time bursts. The 51 multiframe is mainly used for this purpose. Most frames are used for traffic channels (TCH), one of which is shown in detail at the bottom of Figure 9.8. It will be appreciated that a traffic burst will be sent to a particular MS at an agreed time (TS = 2 in this case), once every frame, of which 48 are indicated as passing by during the lifetime of one superframe, etc.

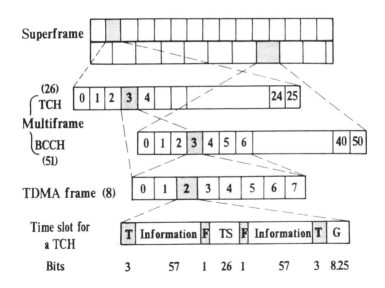

Figure 9.8 The TDMA timing organization hierarchy within GSM

Dealing first with the *traffic channels*, we note that in GSM the speech, or data traffic, is not placed packet-by-packet in successive time slots. Channel coding is used to arrange error-protected speech data into the final form necessary for RF transmission. Channel coding involves adding additional data for channel control, training sequences, and tail/guard bits, shown in Figure 9.9. In addition, the channel coder must interleave the data to enhance the performance of the error correction and rearrange the data into packets for transmission. Training sequence data is added to the TCH which aids in data identification and is also used for equalization of the RF channel. The tail/guard bits provide a buffer between adjacent data packets. Once additional control data has been added by the channel coder, the data is interleaved and arranged into packets for RF transmission (for the TDMA system). It should be noted that after channel coding, the additional data increases the overall data rate. To allow multiple users to share a physical channel, the data is compressed in time and outputted at a much higher data rate, see Figure 9.3, for example.

Figure 9.9 shows that the half-rate error-correction unit increases the bit rate to 22.8 kbps, which was discussed in Chapter 7 (Figure 7.7). The *channel codec* unit, also shown in Figure 9.9, puts the traffic data in 20 msec blocks of 456 b, into smaller blocks of 57 b each.

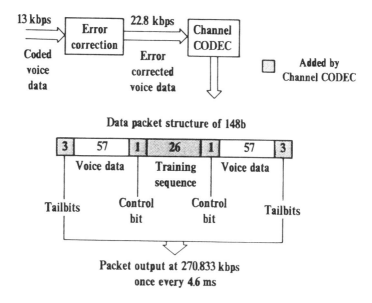

Figure 9.9 Coding arrangement for introducing a burst of coded voice data into a time slot

The 22.8 kbps data is applied to the required TS channel as data in packets of 148 b. The two blocks of 57 bits of voice data are also interleaved by the channel coder to spread out each voice data over eight frames as shown in Figure 9.10. Each packet is then outputted at the much higher data rate of 270.833 kbps, but a packet (length 547 µsec) is only sent once every 4.6 ms.

This is done so that voice data from 8 users can share a physical channel in a TDMA system. Each user sends a packet which uses 1/8th of the total time available on the 270.833 kbps data stream. Once this data has been processed according to Figures 9.8 and 9.10, it is ready to be transmitted via the RF carrier. Note that the 20 msec of speech bits cannot be recovered until after 8 frames have elapsed. This gives rise to the interleaving delay tabulated previously in Table 7.2.

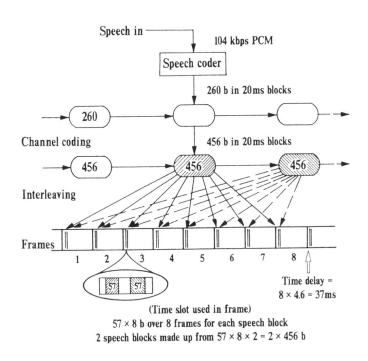

Figure 9.10   Arrangement for interleaving 57 b bursts of coded voice data over eight frames to make up the 20 msec speech burst

Returning to the multiframe shown in Figure 9.8, which has 26 frames, 24 frames are user information. The other two frames carry system control information. A frame consists of eight slots, with each slot assigned to a different mobile terminal.

Coming back to a time slot, we divide 120 ms (multiframe duration) by 26 (frames per multiframe) to obtain 4.62 ms per frame. With the frame divided into eight slots, the slot duration is 577 μs, or 156.25 channel bits, including a guard time of 30.5 μs (8.25 b). No energy is transmitted in the guard interval, which allows the system to operate with variable mobile-to-base arrival times, up to 35 km BS/MS distance being manageable, i.e.

$$\text{delay} \geq \frac{2 \times 35}{3 \times 10^8} \times 10^3 \times 10^6 \approx 23 \ \mu s$$

The two user information bursts of 58 b account for most of the transmission time in a slot. (57 b carry user information, while the other bit is used to distinguish speech from other transmissions.) There is a synchronization burst consisting of 26 b in the middle of the time slot, and the slot begins and ends with three tail bits, all logical zeros.

The GSM modulation is Gaussian minimum shift keying, as described in Chapter 6, in which the modulator bandpass filter has a 3 dB cutoff frequency of 81.25 kHz (0.3 times the bit rate). The modulation efficiency of 271 kbps operating within a 200 kHz carrier spacing is 1.35 bps/Hz. With a bit interval of 3.7 μs, which can exceed typical delay spreads (see Chapter 5), the GSM signal will encounter significant intersymbol interference in the mobile radio multi-path propagation environment. As a consequence, an important component of a GSM receiver is the adaptive equalizer necessary to provide reliable binary signal detection, apart from the channel coding strategies.

9.2.6 Channel coding and training sequence

The channel coding technique chosen for the encoded speech (see Chapter 7) employs a convolution code of rate 1/2, block-diagonally interleaved over 8 TDMA frames to provide protection against burst errors, shown in Figure 9.10.

The bit rate of the resultant protected channel is therefore somewhat higher than that of the speech encoder output at 22.8 kbps, but the traffic channel is now fairly robust and is capable of providing good communication under adverse conditions.

The effect of errors on the signalling, system control messages and data are not the same as for speech, so different coding rates are usually employed in order to provide a balanced degree of protection.

Also, as just described, the long excess delays resulting from signal components, whose paths are very long, result in a measurable delay spread which can only be overcome by using an equalizer in the receivers.

A bit pattern, known as the *training sequence* (TS), the 26 b in Figure 9.9, is transmitted at all times, and the equalizer compares the received bit pattern at each training sequence, adjusting the parameters of a digital filter so as to produce an inverse transfer function to that of the radio path. As the changes are rapid, and because the time slots are independent, every time slot should contain the training sequence.

This is an extra overhead on the information-carrying capacity of the digital channel and further reduces the effective throughput. Without equalization, however, the effective range would be limited to perhaps a few hundred metres; on the other hand, a cheaper mobile station with no equalizer is conceptually possible for very short range operation, e.g. microcell operation.

In the GSM system the design of the equalizer is not specified and is left to each manufacturer, but its performance is defined in terms of a maximum excess delay of 16 µs. The definition is quite complex and is set by type approval conditions.

Type approval is subject to conformance with a set of tests using a system simulator defined in the recommendations. This makes use of a propagation simulator which models a number of multipath profiles together with appropriate Doppler spectra. The models emulate urban, rural and hilly terrain conditions at specified vehicle speeds. A vehicle is anything which physically transports the mobile, including a pedestrian, thus causing it to move in relation to a base station and thereby creating a non-stationary signal reception pattern. The equalizer must perform satisfactorily so that the resultant error performance is within specified tolerances during a type approval test.

9.2.7 Differences required by DCS 1800 specification

The PCN, or DCS 1800 service (see Chapter 8), was deliberately launched with the changes almost totally confined to the radio interface. In fact, as we saw above in Section 9.1, the frequencies of DCS 1800 are twice that of GSM, except that more channels are available. The changes to the DCS 1800 specification, compared to GSM are therefore relatively simple, and are given in Table 9.4.

Table 9.4 Specification change for DCS 1800 as compared to GSM

Definition of the two DCS 1800 handset power classes

Definition of national roaming

Modification of local registration procedure for national roaming

New procedures in the handset for national roaming; changes to the air interface messages to accommodate the large increase of channels for DCS 1800

Definition of DCS 1800 frequency band and performance

Substantial changes to the core GSM specification to define the changes in handset and base station radio performance and especially to allow for a high population density of handsets

Modifications of the link access between handset and base station to allow for the substantial increase in channels for DCS 1800 and to provide the national roaming facility

New messages on the BSC-BTS link arising from the increase in number of channels

Changes to the mobile application point (MAP) to provide national roaming

Definition of conversion of messages between the MAP and air interface

DCS 1800 handset conforming specification

Specification of DCS 1800 directory on the SIM; changes to the SIM to allow for the increase in number of channels

DCS 1800 base station specification

DCS 1800 system simulator conformity specification

Details of the power classes were in fact listed above in Table 9.2. The 1800 MHz cellular PLMN service (or indeed the PCS 1900 services), are aimed at chiefly microcellular (dense urban operation), but the specifications do not limit the service. It could be said that the limitation is more the radio range. In fact dual-band phones, e.g. 900/1800 operation, are in the process of being released.

9.2.8 Connecting to the system

An interesting consideration at this stage, if one contemplates Figure 9.10, for example, is how does a subscriber, who switches on his handset, synchronize to the activity of the base station signals? These signals are individual RF signal bursts on one of the RF channels, (Figure 8.2). An alternative view is that of Figure 9.11. This shows the activity from a BS, which could be serving up to eight MSs. In the diagram, time slots number 0 and 4 show no traffic. The shape of the time slot burst profile is tightly defined (see Figure 9.14 below), but can have different power levels – to sort out the near-far problem and minimize the C/I ratio.

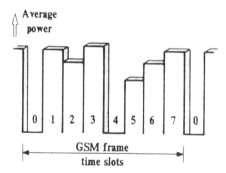

Figure 9.11 Example for the power profile for a GSM base station

How does the MS joining the system line up with this tightly tiered activity? Again, as in analog systems there has to be beacon channels or frequencies. In fact, in laying out a service one channel has always to be allocated to carry a *beacon channel*, and is one of the principal *GSM radio interface logical channels*, called the *broadcast control channel* (BCCH). A mobile must first find this burst signal (in free space), before he can send or receive. This is not enough, however. The MS must synchronize in frequency, because of the strict modulation strategy, and in time, so he follows bit by bit, in every time slot, for example. The BCCH channel is always assigned four consecutive time slots number 0, within a 51 multiframe (see Figure 9.8). This enables the MS to get some idea of the frame timing, but more importantly, now knows where to look for:

(i)   the *frequency correction channel* (FCCH)

(ii) the *synchronization channel* (SCH)

Both of these have distinctive time slot structures, and also a known position within a multiframe, in relation to the BCCH. The MS finds the FCCH burst, and then knows that the SCH will be eight frames later, again in time slot 0.

The structures of the FCCH and SCH time slots are shown in Figure 9.12, together with a normal (traffic) channel (TCH) burst, and the access burst (ACH), which actually only comes from a MS to a BS, but of course needs to comply to the same timing constraints.

The FCCH is simply a burst of 142 zero bits plus 6 zero tail bits. A MS can easily recognize this continuous FSK marker frequency (1625/24 = higher than the nominal channel carrier frequency (related to the ARFCH), and can correct its own internal oscillators (see Figure 9.3). The FCCH burst also sets the time boundaries of subsequent time slots, which in this particular instance is TS 0. The MS receiver can now look for the SCH.

The SCH has an extended training sequence (64 b). This sequence has very well defined correlation properties and can precisely define bit times in a burst, then used subsequently. At the same time, the SCH provides the MS with full details of the slot numbers of the multiframes.

The SCH also provides a further service, in the form of a *base station identity code* (BSIC). This is a 6 b code word which actually first carries a *colour code* identification, in much the same way as for analog cellular (see Figure 1.15). In this way a mobile station, which is resident in an area where the lack of GSM frequencies means that the same BCCH channel could be being used in nearby clusters, or indeed in different networks, may be distinguished.

At the end of this activity (the user will be familiar with the wait after switching on), the mobile can read with some certainty the messages on the BCCH. These consist of the network identity, the applicable location area code and even information on the surrounding cells. The MS will now indicate to the user which particular network he has camped on. More than one PLMN may be actually working in a particular location. The user will usually go to his home network.

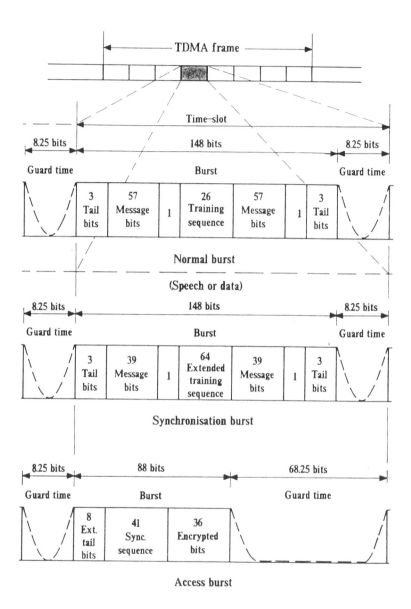

Figure 9.12   The detailed structure of the principal bursts occurring within the GSM air interface

9.2.9 Signalling within GSM

There are many types of control channel. The main ones are: a *broadcast control channel* (BCCH) on down-link only, to keep MSs aware of the base station identity, frequency allocation and frequency hopping, if used; a *common control channel* (CCCH), further subdivided to provide a *random access channel* (RACH) on the up-link; a *paging channel* (PCH) and an *access grant channel* (AGCH) on the down-link; a *dedicated control channel* (DCCH) for registration, location updating, authentication and call set-up; two *associated control channels* (ACCH), one a continuous stream *slow* ACCH (SACCH) for call supervision and burst stealing mode; one a *fast* ACCH (FACCH) for power control and handover. These channels are logically mapped on to the physical RF channel, as shown in Figure 9.13.

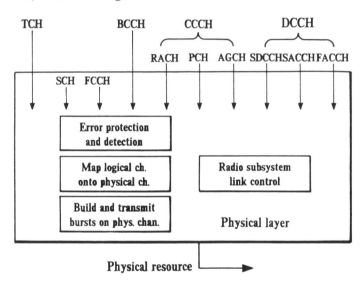

Figure 9.13 Mapping of the logical channels onto the physical RF channel

Notice, in particular, the *traffic channel* (TCH) outside the logical resources, whereas the BCCH, FCCH and the SCH are closely associated, as just discussed.

The SACCH is carried in one frame of every 120 ms multiframe. Each active terminal owns a slot in the SACCH frame. A SACCH message contains 184 information bits. Error control coders process this information to produce 456 channel bits which are interleaved and distributed over four time slots. With one time slot per multiframe, and a multiframe duration of 120 ms, the total transmission time of a SACCH message is 480 ms. Thus the transmission bit rate is 456 b in 480 ms, or 950 bps. The information rate is 184 b in 480 ms or 383 bps.

When more rapid network control is required, GSM creates a *fast associated control channel* (FACCH) by interrupting user information for a duration of four frames. The delivery time of a FACCH message is four frames, or 18.5 ms, in contrast to 480 ms in the SACCH.

Table 9.5 GSM radio interface logical channels

Channel name	Channel type	Usage
Broadcast Control Channel (BCCH)	Broadcast downlink	Carries a system information used by mobiles in the idle mode, e.g. network identity, current location area code, information on surrounding cells.
Synchronization Channel (SCH)	Broadcast downlink	Used by mobiles to achieve time synchronization with the BTS
Frequency Correction Channel (FCCH)	Broadcast downlink	Used by mobiles to achieve frequency synchronization with the BTS
Cell Broadcast Channel (CBCH)	Common downlink	Carries cell broadcast short messages
Paging Channel (PCH)	Common downlink	Carries paging messages to alert mobiles to incoming calls or messages
Access Grant Channel (AGCH)	Common downlink	Assigns mobiles to specific channels for dedicated operation
Random Access Channel (RACH)	Common uplink	Used by a mobile to request resources for a subsequent operation, e.g. to establish a call or perform a location update
Fast Associated Control Channel (FACCH)	Dedicated uplink and downlink	A high rate signalling channel, used during call establishment, subscriber authentication, and for handover commands
Slow Associated Control Channel (SACCH)	Dedicated uplink and downlink	A low rate signalling channel associated with each traffic channel, used for non-critical signalling such as radio measurement data
Stand-alone Dedicated Control Channel (SDCCH)	Dedicated uplink and downlink	A signalling channel which can be used independently of calls when signalling alone is required, e.g. for location updates, short messages, supplementary services management
Traffic channel full (TCH/F)	Dedicated uplink and downlink	Carries full rate (13 kbps) speech, or data at 12, 6 or 3.6 kbps
Traffic channel half (TCH/H)	Dedicated uplink and downlink	Carries half rate (7 kbps) speech, or data at 6 or 3.6 kbps

The BCCH is organized into a 51-frame multiframe as shown earlier in Figure 9.8, and is carried in time slot zero on a non-hopping radio frequency carrier; the remaining time slots are available for traffic channels. Several radio frequency carriers are allocated to a BS, one of which will carry the BCCH. The use of hopping or non-hopping radio frequency carriers for the traffic channels is optional.

One channel which is associated with the up-link path only, is the *random access channel* (RACH),. This is rather differently formatted burst, as shown last in Figure 9.12 above. It has to be shorter since a MS may make a request to a BS, which is near, or far away, and needs to guarantee that its burst falls within the listening TS of the BS. Likewise the training sequence, after the extended lead-in time (the extra tail bits) allows the BS to be prepared for the encrypted path information bits. The delay required is then made by the BS so that the signalling can continue with normally structured bits.

Unlike analog cellular, the traffic messages and the signalling messages are part and parcel of the same frame make-up arrangement within GSM. It is therefore perhaps useful to go over these time slots and channels, as they are called, again, so that the correspondence to analog cellular becomes more obvious. To do this, we use Table 9.5 on the previous page.

It is also worth noting the access request from a subscriber, although the random access channel must be controlled in order to avoid blocking situations. Among the different means available, the most efficient is through the *access class number*. In each subscriber's SIM card a random number from 1 to 10 is stored. In the event of saturation the BSC can restrict, through the broadcast channel, the access to any class of subscribers. Special class numbers (11 to 15) are reserved for high priority subscribers (security services, emergency services, operator field staff, etc.).

9.2.10 Radio link management

The radio link, comprising both uplink and downlink, has to be managed in order to ensure continuity of service and to minimise interference to other users of the system. The main aspects are addressed here.

Timing advance: the propagation time of the radio signals between the MS and the BS will be determined by the distance that the radio signal travels. Since cells in the GSM system may vary in size from perhaps 1-2 km up to about 35 km, we saw that the propagation time can vary from about 3-30 microseconds. In order that the data bursts transmitted by each MS fall *exactly* into the time slot structure at the BS receiver it is necessary to advance the timing of the MS transmitter by an appropriate amount and this must be done individually for each MS. This is done at call set-up by the BS, which measures the round trip time and sends a timing advance message to the MS, which is amended, when necessary, at intervals during operation.

Power ramping: the power burst of all GSM transmitters must be very tightly controlled. Unlike analog cellular, where the transmitter mask specification relates to power versus frequency (see Figure 8.1), in GSM a very specific power ramp-up and power ramp-down mask has to be specified for just one time slot of 148 b occupying 542.8 μsec. This mask is shown in Figure 9.14.

This mask ignores the 8.25 guard bits period, which is built-in for the timing advance procedure, and also loses half of the first and last tail bits so in effect there are only 147 useful bits. This specification has to be met at the same time as the power frequency mask (Figure 8.1), which is a function of the GMSK modulator performance.

Adaptive power control: this is applied to all MSs to ensure that they operate at the lowest power level consistent with adequate received signal strength and quality. The power is controlled in steps of 2 dB from the maximum defined by the power class.

For example, a class 1 MS (peak power 20 W or 43 dBm as shown in Table 9.2) has 15 steps giving a minimum power level of 13 dBm. The other classes are catered for by the same algorithm since their peak powers, 8 W (39 dBm), 5 W (37 dBm) and 2 W (33 dBm), all correspond to steps on the same scale.

Power control is achieved by a process which involves measurement, by the MS, of the received signal strength, quality and the regular reporting, on the uplink, of these data to the BS. The BS has preset parameters to enable a decision to be made and, when a threshold is reached, it commands the MS to change power level either upwards or downwards as necessary. The received quality is measured by the BER.

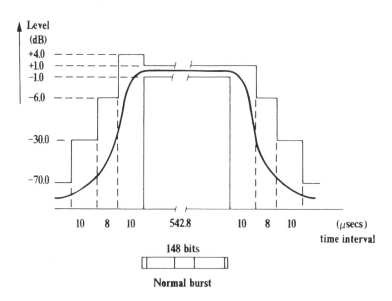

Figure 9.14 GSM transmitter power ramp specification

Base stations may have an adjustable peak power level to allow the system operator to make adjustments to the cell coverage area and in addition they may employ power control on the downlink in a similar way to that defined for MSs. This makes the power profile of any BS complex over successive GSM frames, an example being given in Figure 9.11. Each component of the profile must meet the specification of Figure 9.14.

Handover: this is one of the basic features of cellular radio and enables MSs to move freely across cell boundaries and enjoy continuous service. It uses the same process of measurement and reporting as for power control; indeed the two procedures are closely linked.

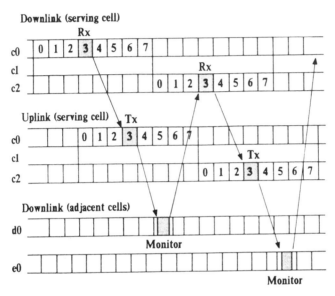

Figure 9.15 Mobile station usage of channels during a call, showing monitoring of adjacent cell broadcast control channel time slots, and frequency hopping if used

The GSM system exploits the properties of TDMA very effectively for handover; the MS listens for the BCCH of up to 6 surrounding BSs in the time slots that are not being used for transmission or reception, see Figure 9.15. It forms a list of up to 6 handover candidates and reports the signal strength and quality to the serving BS. Meanwhile the BS is also monitoring the signal strength and quality on the serving channel. Handover is under the control of the network, usually the base station controllers, and is used to provide continuity of communication by the availability of another channel which can allow communication at a lower power level. Handover can also be used for traffic balancing between cells.

Handover to another cell will involve returning to another radio frequency channel, but handover is also possible to a different time slot on the same radio frequency channel in the same cell, which may be used for interference control reasons. In each case one has *mobile assisted handover*. Because handover is so closely related to the GSM numbering plan, it is best to talk about these numbers first.

9.2.11 Network numbering hierarchy

Since the mobile network is considered to be an extension of the fixed network, the subscriber must conform to the PSTN/ISDN numbering plan of a country. Hence every mobile subscriber will have a *mobile station international ISDN number* (MSISDN), the number one would find in the phone book. However, to improve privacy for the subscriber, GSM also defines another number, known as the *international mobile subscriber identification* (IMSI), which is mapped to the MSISDN by the operator. The IMSI is used in the mobile related signalling transactions. The structures of the MSISDN and IMSI are given below.

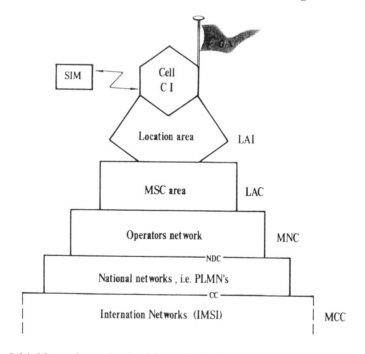

Figure 9.16 Network numbering hierarchy in the GSM system

To assist in the creation of the MSISDN and IMSI, and facilitate tracking of mobiles, there is a hierarchy of numbers used in a GSM PLMN, as illustrated in Figure 9.16. These numbers are defined as follows:

CC: country code

MCC: mobile country code. Used to identify the home country of the PLMN within the IMSI.

NDC: national destination code. Uniquely identifies a PLMN in a country for use in the MSISDN.

MNC: mobile network code. Identifies a GSM PLMN in a country for use in the IMSI.

LAC: location area code. Identifies a location area (group of cells) in a PLMN; up to 2 octets in length.

LAI: location area identity. Similar to the LAC, but with unique international identification made up of MCC+MNC+LAC.

CI: cell identity. Defines a cell or sector; 2 octets maximum length.

CGI: cell global identity. Sent on the BCCH and provides a PLMN based cell identity; made up of LAI+CI.

The above numbers relate to the area and networks; on the other hand a variety of numbers relate to the subscriber and the mobile equipment in use. The interactions between these numbers and the network numbers is as follows:

SN: subscriber's number, associated with the SIM card and unique to the user.

MSISDN: mobile station international ISDN number; equivalent to your telephone's publicized number. It consists of the CC, NDC, *home location register identity* (HLRID), and Subscriber Number (SN), as shown here.

2	3	7
CC	NDC	SN

HLRID
2 digits

MSIN: mobile station identification number, which uniquely identifies a subscriber within a home PLMN, as shown here.

2	8
HLRID	SN

IMSI: international mobile subscriber identification, known only to the operator to ensure subscriber confidentiality. A unique IMSI is allocated to the MSISDN. The IMSI is used for setting up signalling connections. It consists of the MCC, PLMN code, HLRID and MSIN.

TMSI: temporary mobile station identification; allocated by the VLR after authentication and used on the radio path. It gives protection from intruders listening on the signalling link; hence the TMSI is normally used in paging (though the IMSI can also be used). TMSI is more efficient, being a smaller number.

To guard against double allocating TMSIs, the number includes a time stamp and the access index, which identifies the MS in the VLR. The TMSI can be reallocated at any time, but is usually changed during the location updating procedure[*]. Reallocation would occur when the radio link is in a ciphered mode to prevent eavesdropping. The LAI is used together with the TMSI to uniquely identify a subscriber. Both numbers are sent to the network by the mobile during the start of a location update procedure described below.*

LMSI: local mobile station identification, used by the VLR database to search for subscriber details. It is the temporary address of the location containing the subscriber data.

MSRN: mbile station roaming number facilitates the routing of a traffic channel from the gateway MSC (GMSC) to the visited MSC (VMSC). The MSRN has a maximum of 15 digits, made up from the CC, NDC and an individual number related to the ISDN telephone numbering plan, shown here:

2	3	= <10
CC	NDC	number

HON: handover number is a unique number used to establish a connection when there is an MSC to MSC handover. It provides routing information and is generated by the target VLR during the handover process.

Subscriber data, such as the IMSI, class of service, VLR address and directory number are held in the HLR/AC, which is normally centralized in the subscriber's home network. The roaming subscriber's mobile must have its location information in the HLR updated by means of the local (visited) network signalling back to the HLR the necessary data, because it is the HLR that is accessed for location information at the start of a call set up procedure. The HLR is kept updated with the mobile's location and capability details via the location update procedure.

While the HLR is able to offer location information to the network, when (say) a call is to be set up, the traffic connection within the terrestrial part of the PLMN is determined by the MSRN. The MSRN, which has ISDN numbering information for the destination point, is extracted by the HLR from the visited VLR and sent to the source MSC. This process is best illustrated by an example.

Thus, in Figure 9.17 the information flow relating to a mobile terminated call is shown. The steps in the process are as follows:

• The caller dials the MSISDN of the subscriber to be contacted. The call is routed to the nearest GSM gateway (GMSC) in the country of origin.

• The GMSC interrogates the HLR over a common channel signalling mobile application part (MAP) link by sending the MSISDN to the HLR.

[*] Ciphering and authentication are described in section 9.2.4.

- If the subscriber has no restrictions the HLR requests, via a C7 link, an MSRN from the VLR. At the same time the HLR sends the MSISDN, IMSI, LMSI, and optionally the MSC number, to the VLR in order to update the database. The LMSI is the address of the transient subscriber data in the VLR and enables faster access for the HLR. The VLR obtains the LAC.

- The VLR sends the MSRN to the HLR.

- The MSRN is transferred to the GMSC, which uses it to perform routing to the area where the MS was roaming when the last location update was executed.

- The GMSC selects a trunk to the visited MSC. If it is foreign, the PSTN and associated signalling systems required for that connection would be deployed.

- The VMSC sends a page request message to the BSS.

- The MS is paged in the location area over the paging channel (PCH).

- The MS responds on the random access channel (RACH).

- A traffic channel is set up with end to end connectivity, enabling speech or data exchange to commence. The aspects of the call set-up relating to authentication, ciphering and alerting are not shown in the diagram

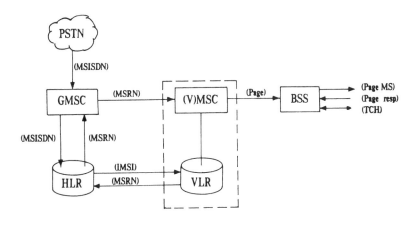

Figure 9.17 Number management in a mobile terminated call

Two points in this description need further clarification. Firstly, the concept location updating (which will happen at every handover), and secondly, the matter of authentication and voice channel encryption.

9.2.12 Location updating

The cell global identity number was shown at the top of Figure 9.16, since this is the position of the mobile. If the MS moves to another cell location (deemed better), he will 'drag' all the numbers with him. If this is a single national network, then the location updating procedure falls into the following categories:

a) first location update (mobile is turned on, or SIM card is inserted)
b) the MS moves within the same VLR area, but to a new location
c) the MS moves to a new VLR area, which is a neighbour
d) the MS moves to a new VLR area, which is not a neighbour
e) expiry of periodic location update timer

In all cases the parameters which are updated in the VLR are the *LMSI*, IMSI, MSISDN, HLR address, *TMSI, LAI, KcSN* and the subscription details of the MS. The numbers in italics are really the only ones which change. The importance of the numbering hierarchy is very clear. The relocating activity will often be brought about by handover.

9.2.13 Measuring radio conditions for handover

Handover can be defined as the directed change of the radio channel used by the mobile to communicate with the network in order to maintain a good quality of service. A base station continuously monitors the performance of the link between the base station and mobile and instigates a handover to a better channel if required. For the uplink, this is achieved by using parameters measured by the base station; for the downlink the mobile takes the measurements and regularly reports them to the base station. This method of mobile reported measurements is the *mobile assisted handover* (MAHO) shown in Figure 9.15 above where *actual* measurements of the radio environment around the mobile are used, rather than the base station making estimations based on the uplink only.

For the GSM reference model, different types of handover can be defined. These are:

- Intra cell handover – between traffic channels in the same cell

- Inter cell handover – between traffic channels in different cells
- Inter BSC handover – between traffic channels associated with BTSs connected to different BSCs
- Inter MSC – between traffic channels associated with different MSCs
- Inter PLMN – between traffic channels in different networks

The handover strategy is critical in the design of a GSM network, since the subscriber is unable to detect whether he is moving from a good to a poor coverage area (except by looking at the bars on his handset). The subscriber will not want to know about 'holes' in the network coverage and therefore the handover strategies, and an ample supply of base stations, needs to be good. The parameters for candidate handover selection can only be listed here. Their exact algorithm is a specialized activity as can be ascertained by the reported parameters now described.

Measurements made by the mobile are sent to the base station over the SACCH, which can be associated with a TCH or SDCCH. The latter facilitates the handover process while the mobile is in the signalling state. A complete SACCH block of data is received by the base station every 480 ms. Each measurement is averaged over the SACCH block period. In addition to reports relevant to the downlink from the serving cell, the mobile also reports the received level of the six strongest surrounding, or neighbour cells, as well as their base station identity codes, which can be decoded from the SCH on the BCCH of the neighbouring cells. The list of reported parameters is as follows:

Received signal strength downlink
Received signal quality downlink
Downlink neighbour cell
BSIC of neighbour cell
Channel number

The base station would make measurements of the uplink. Uplink parameters for a reliable handover evaluation are:

Received signal strength uplink
Received signal quality uplink
MS-BTS distance
Power budget
Interference level in unallocated time slots

At the base station, the handover decision process involves an algorithm that uses the above information and runs in real time. Every mobile-to-base dedicated link requires a unique handover process to be run, thereby making the handover process quite demanding on base station resources.

9.2.14 Security management

A feature which the planners of GSM were very anxious to build into the system was security for both the network and for the subscriber. For the network, this means that only authentic users can gain access to the network. Also it is not possible for an outside party to remotely track a MS. For the user, his voice and data messages are fully encrypted on the radio access path and eavesdropping of calls is not feasible.

Authentication is performed by asking the terminal to give the result of a specific computation made on a random number (RAND) sent by the system and then comparing the result with what it should be.

This computation process is dependent on a secret key (Ki) specific to each subscriber SIM card. The computation is done following a ciphering algorithm A3, whose property is only that knowing the result (SRES) and one input (RAND), the other input (Ki) cannot be practically deduced. The secret key (Ki) and the A3 algorithm are stored with protection in the SIM card, and in the HLR, both elements performing the calculation shown in Figure 9.18.

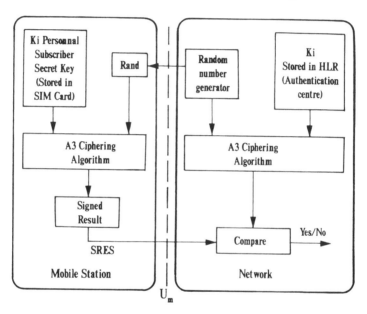

Figure 9.18   Authentication for a GSM telephone using the key code Ki stored in the SIM card

The ciphering of the traffic channel is achieved with a second ciphering algorithm A5 applied to a key (Kc) chosen for each connection and a number changed at each burst.

The key Kc is computed in the terminal and in the HLR with a third algorithm A5 similar to A3, shown in detail in Figure 9.19. The A3 and A5 algorithms are not specified in GSM/DCS recommendations, but are left to the choice of the operator.

The personal number of a subscriber (IMSI) is not ciphered, to avoid complexity in managing the preliminary dialogue between the terminal and the infrastructure. Protection of the subscriber identity is achieved by using the TMSI allocated by the network the first time that the mobile registers in a given area.

9.2.15 *Personal mobility aspects*

The ability for a person to carry his/her cellular subscription capability, without a mobile phone, anywhere in a coverage area is referred to as personal mobility. In GSM, this is realized by the *subscriber identity module* (SIM) card, which contains all the individual subscriber information. The SIM can be carried separately from the mobile equipment (ME), if need be.

The subscriber can use the SIM with any mobile since the SIM-ME interface is standardized by GSM. When a SIM is removed, the mobile becomes unusable for normal services, but can still be used for emergency calls. Even though a number of different mobiles may be used by the same SIM, billing will always be attributed to the owner's account. Prepaid SIM facilities are being explored, rather like phone cards.

This personal mobility, or *roaming*, is the feature which has really put GSM on the map, so to speak. The fact that there are over 130, and more, operators having reached roaming agreement potential, encourages GSM roll-out. DCS 1800 is following. Its later start has meant that the roaming agreements have not yet all been put in place.

The users' view of roaming when abroad can be summarized as follows:

- Registration
  MS switches on
  Mobile finds a network (BCCH)
  Network verifies identity of mobile, i.e. authentication procedure
  Mobile accepted as a visitor and also the VLR data set up

- Incoming call
  Outside PSTN party dials mobile number (MSISDN)
  Call routed to the GSM mobile according to the numbers and activities of Figure 9.17

- Outgoing call
  Mobile calls local PSTN number, which could include home mobiles
  Mobile accesses for international and proceeds with required county code, etc. This would be either the foreign PSTN or a MSISDN mobile number

We dealt with registration in Figure 9.18. The main difference is that the MS, with its valid SIM card is now under the control of a 'foreign' serving switch (overseas HLR), this later switch having obtained the appropriate authentication data from the mobile's home network.

For either incoming, or outgoing calls, this authentication activity has to be in place first. Figure 9.20, which should be compared to Figure 9.18, shows the activity required. This could be followed by the outgoing call procedure, Figure 9.21, if this is required.

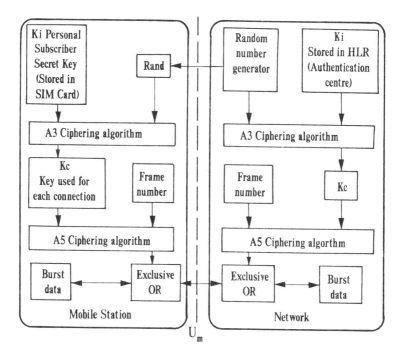

Figure 9.19 Ciphering algorithm for encoding the traffic channel using a temporary cipher key Kc

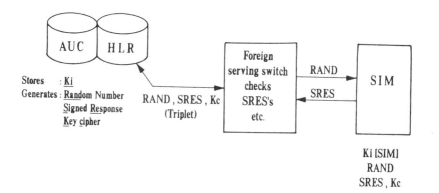

Figure 9.20 Authentication procedure upon registration of a GSM phone in a foreign network, which has roaming agreement

A final point, in comparison to the PSTN, dual tone multi-frequency tones are generated on the speech path by pressing the number keys of the telephone set. The specification of the GSM mobile station requests that DTMF tones are not generated by the MS, but by the MSC, to avoid going through speech keys encoding. Instead, signalling messages are sent when pressing keys on the mobile station side, and tones are generated by the MSC at the reception of such messages. This applies only for transmission from the mobile station. This does not preclude sending DTMF tones to the MS; they will go through the 13 kbps encoding. The procedure is not that simple, however, because the period during which a tone is generated is under the control of the user, and it is considered necessary that the MSC acknowledges these messages. As the result, the sending of one tone requires four messages. This is repeated for each tone, resulting in a total of 40 messages for the sending of one ten-digit number. The strategy does, of course, allow compatibility with the existing world-wide PSTN operations.

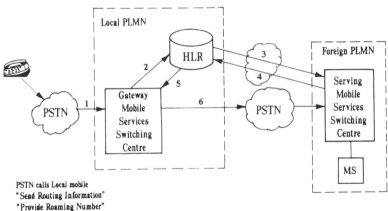

1   PSTN calls Local mobile
2   "Send Routing Information"
3   "Provide Roaming Number"
4 & 5 Return of roaming number/Routing Information
6   Call established to serving switch

Figure 9.21   Procedure within the home and a foreign GSM network necessary to set up a call to a roaming GSM subscriber

The short message service (SMS) provision of GSM, on the other hand, is more direct. The message can be 'typed up' on the MS screen; it is then sent on command as a message burst on the authenticated traffic channel as an SMS message. SMS *service centres* (SCs) within the recipient network (of the party called) will hold, or forward, these messages when practical to do so.

Part 2: The North American digital cellular designs

9.3 D-AMPS

The digital cellular radio system developed for North America differs from GSM in several ways. Two underlying reasons for the differences are found in the most pressing requirements of each system and in their regulatory constraints. While a principal purpose of GSM was to establish, for the first time, a unified public telephone system for Europe, the United States and Canada had the benefit of a single standard (AMPS) since the introduction of cellular services in the early 1980s. GSM was designed as a stand-alone system operating in specially assigned frequency bands, but any new North American digital transmission techniques had to co-exist with the analog systems in the established cellular frequency bands, and also offer operation in the PCS bands.

The development of the North American digital transmission standard came at a time of high demand for cellular services, with no new spectrum available to meet this demand. Therefore, the overriding aim of the technology was to increase the capacity of the existing spectrum so as to provide increased services. In 1988, encouraged by the *Cellular Telecommunication Industry Association* (CTIA), consisting mainly of cellular service providers, the *Telecommunication Industry Association* (TIA) of equipment manufacturers established a technical committee to develop a digital standard. Like GSM, the TIA stimulated the production of prototype equipment, which was then subjected to field trials (access and modulation technologies) and laboratory tests (speech coders). In 1989, the industry, by a majority vote, adopted specific aspects of the dual-mode system, and in 1990 it accepted the entire transmission standard which is referred to as the Electronics Industry Association Interim Standard 54. Hence, the name IS-54, which, at this time, is the basic forward and backward looking new technology for the D-AMPS.

9.3.1 Radio transmission strategy

The carrier spacing of IS-54 is 30 kHz, as in the first generation AMPS system. Operating companies will selectively convert analog channels to digital operation in order to relieve traffic congestion at cellular base stations, or to introduce digital technology into their service. The basic TDMA structure of D-AMPS was shown earlier in Figure 8.5. Each digital channel operates at 48.6 kbps, carrying three user signals. The ADC or D-AMPS air-interface parameters are shown in Table 9.6, which should be compared with GSM in Table 9.3 on page 203.

Table 9.6 D-AMPS air-interface parameters

Mobile to BS	824-849 MHz
BS to mobile	869-894 MHz
Channel spacing	30 kHz
R$_X$/T$_X$ spacing - frequency	45 MHz
R$_X$/T$_X$ spacing - time	1.85 ms
Modulation	π/4 DQPSK
Users per frequency pair	3
Frame period	20 ms
Time slot period	6.6667 ms
Symbol period	41.15 μs
Symbols/time slot	162
Transmission rate	48.6 kbps

From the frame/time slot structure of ADC shown now in more detail in Figure 9.22, note how control and traffic data are combined within each time slot. This saves on overheads, and is a less complicated frame hierarchy when compared to GSM.

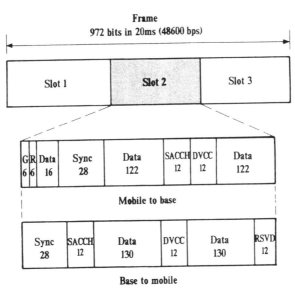

Frame
972 bits in 20ms (48600 bps)

Figure 9.22 IS-54 time slot and frame structure (for definitions see text)

A time slot carries 324 b including 260 b of user information and 12 b (= SACCH), of user control information. The remaining 52 b carry a *time synchronization signal* 28 b (= SYNC), a *digital verification colour code* 12 b (= DVCC) and, in the mobile-to-base direction, a 6 b guard time interval, when no energy is transmitted, followed by a 6 b (= R) ramp interval to allow the transmitter to reach its full output power level. 12 b (= RSVD) are reserved in the forward time slot.

The 28 b synchronization field (SYNC) contains a known bit pattern that allows the receiver to establish bit synchronization and to train an adaptive equalizer. The system specifies six different synchronization patterns, one for each slot in 40 ms of frame. This allows the receiver to lock on to its assigned time slots. The digital verification colour code plays the role of the supervisory audio tone as in the analog AMPS system. There are 256 (8) b colour codes, protected by a (12;8;3) Hamming code. Each base station is assigned one of these codes and the verification procedure prevents a receiver from locking on to an interfering signal from a distant cell.

The IS-54 speech coder is described in Chapter 7 as a codebook vocoder and, as shown in Figure 7.10, processes input signals in blocks of duration 20 ms, just as in GSM. Also, in common with GSM, the transmitter assembles 40 ms of speech information and interleaves the bits in order to spread short bursts of channel errors over a longer time interval. Because of the different coding rate and timing structure, 40 ms of speech information (520 b) goes into two IS-54 time slots, rather than the eight slots of GSM.

An important feature of D-AMPS is that there is no common control channel; the standard uses the AMPS FCC channel. In this way dual mode mobiles can be directed to an analog or a digital AMPS service. If it is D-AMPS then the SACCH bits give user specific information. During handover a FACCH signal is substituted in place of a speech data block.

In a departure from the constant envelope modulations of first generation cellular radio systems and other second generation systems, ADC adopts a linear modulation technique, namely, a variant of differential phase shift keying, as described in Chapter 6.

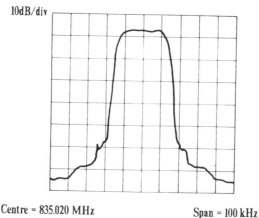

Centre = 835.020 MHz   Span = 100 kHz

Figure 9.23 The RF spectrum of a D-AMPS π/4 QPSK signal

The transmission rate is 48.6 kbps, with a channel spacing of 30 kHz; this comes to 1.62 bps/Hz, a 20% improvement over GSM. The main penalty of linear modulation was linear PA technology, but this has now been solved. The specific method of modulation is π/4 DQPSK, with root-cosine rolloff filtering at the transmitter and receiver. The rolloff factor is 0.35, which provides a spectral zero in the transmitted signal at 16.4 kHz. The spectral containment of this modulation is illustrated in Figure 9.23.

9.3.2 Control channels

As a dual-mode system, in the sense that both analog and digital MSs can have access to the system, IS-54 retains much of the control structure of the original AMPS system. Call set-up is provided by forward control channels and reverse control channels, which carry messages between base stations and mobile telephones. Augmenting the original message set is an indication that a mobile terminal has dual-mode capability. When a call is established with a dual-mode terminal, the system has the option of assigning this call to a digital channel. The system also has the capability to hand-off a dual-mode mobile from an analog voice channel to a digital channel, and vice versa. When operating over a digital channel, the dual-mode terminal exchanges messages with the system through the SACCH and the FACCH, as in GSM. The control channel messages have a length of 65 b, and the FACCH in IS-54 operates in a way similar to its counterpart in GSM, by interrupting user information to send urgent control messages. In the FACCH, forward error-correction is provided by a convolutional coder, that produces 260 b which replace the user information in one time slot. In the case of the SACCH, there is a half-rate convolutional coder that generates 132 b per message. This information is interleaved over 12 time slots and transmitted in the SACCH fields shown in Figure 9.22. The total delay of the SACCH is twelve IS-54 frames, or 240 ms.

Like GSM, mobile assisted hand-off is again practical and used in D-AMPS, since again the mobile can measure signal strengths of other BSs in the spare time slots. A guard space G, corresponding to six symbol periods, is to prevent adjoining time slots, transmitted by mobile units, from colliding at the base stations. Such collisions may occur if the time slots have variations in propagation time on the way to the base station. The base station can adjust the transmission from the mobile unit in steps of half a symbol period by sending time alignment messages. The length of the guard time is set to avoid collisions in cells with a radius of up to approximately 10 miles. Thus, there is no need to fine tune the mobile unit transmission during handover between cells of normal size. If the mobile unit is to send a shortened burst as its first signal to the base station, it is told so in the handover command. This first signal has been introduced solely to determine how the transmission time of the mobile unit needs to be adjusted.

Finally, it is important to note that the IS-54 standard has now been updated to IS-136. This allows D-AMPS to offer short messaging, broadcast messaging, group addressing and a paging channel format, which supports a 'sleep mode', as found in pagers, i.e. section 4.4.

9.3.3 *D-AMPS network architecture*

The US TIA also specified a network architecture, known as IS-41, which underwrites the basis for mobility management for AMPS and D-AMPS. The basic architecture is shown in Figure 9.24.

One notes the very strong parallel with the GSM network plan, Figure 9.4. A description of the network entities need not therefore be repeated.

A notable difference, however, is the absence of the *base station subsystem* (BSS = BTS + BSC). The BSS (which could include a TRAU) took some of the load and functionality off the MSC in GSM. In D-AMPS, dual mode operation with AMPS, needed to be maintained, i.e. the MSC would be serving AMPS and D-AMPS users at the same time. Also an MSC here may need to direct PSTN calls, and not rely on a GMSC. GSM is known as an *open standard*; D-AMPS is rather more constrained because of its desire for backward compatibility, but this has not prevented the major switch by manufacturers to include all the necessary features in the MSC, whether they be one for a network, or several for a distributed network.

For example, the newer cell strategy features, which are discussed at the end of the next chapter, such as hierarchical cell structures, frequency hopping and adaptive channel allocation, can all be supported.

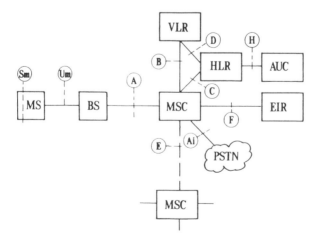

Figure 9.24 The IS-41 network structure

Another important requirement for an MSC, which has connections to the PSTN, is the possibility of an echo caused by delay in the speaker/listener path and unbalancing of a 4-wire to a 2-wire telephone connection. As long as the delay of the transmission path is short, the reflected speech energy is not a problem; it will then only be added to the normal taker sidetone present in all handsets, but when the delay is increased and the reflected speech energy becomes separated from the sidetone, it will be perceived as an echo, the so-called talker echo.

Delay is introduced in the transmission path as a consequence of propagation time over long distances and/or the coding of the transmitted signals. The most obvious cause of delay is the use of satellites: a geostationary satellite causes a one-way transmission delay of 260 ms, and the total echo path delay will consequently exceed 520 ms. Further, as was set out in Table 7.2, delay is part and parcel of digital cellular systems, where it is caused by the speech and channel coding necessary for radio transmission. This coding results in a one-way transmission delay of typically 100 ms when blocks of speech samples are transmitted over the air interface. The delay of both these applications is well above the value of 25 ms, at which the CCITT recommends the use of echo control devices, or echo cancelling.

Echo cancellers are complex devices and also have to be such that they do not add further distortion into the speech path. The method used today is to have a pool of echo cancellers, which can be added into the MSC exit terminal circuit when circuit unbalance and echo is apparent. The scheme is illustrated in Figure 9.25.

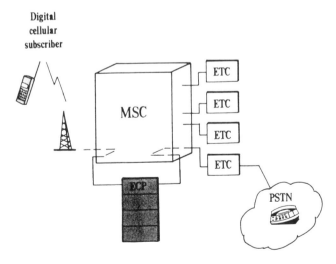

ETC – Exchange terminal circuit
ECP – Echo canceller in pool

Figure 9.25 Echo cancellers in a pool added to an MSC exchange

This arrangement has clearly a number of advantages over putting an echo canceller in every path, whether it be needed or not.

9.3.4 North American PCS plans

The concept of personal communication services was introduced in Chapter 8, Section 8.4.2. In the USA the matter is more complicated than the DCS 1800 option now in operation in the UK, i.e. see section 9.2.7. To help us go forward, the best way is to look at the frequency plans, Figure 9.26.

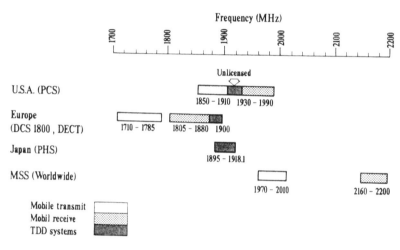

Figure 9.26 Regional and international wireless frequency allocations near 2 GHz

We look first at the DCS 1800 allocations (in Europe, at least and also Region 3); these frequencies are the ones set out at the end of section 9.1. At the top of the band, we find DECT, a sophisticated cordless telephony system, akin to the Japanese PHS, both described towards the end of this chapter. *Mobile satellite services* (MSS) frequencies are also shown in the diagram, mainly for general reference.

Focusing now on the USA PCS frequencies, they are clearly out of line with the above services, but since the Americas are in their own well separated radio region 2 (Figure 1.9), this does not matter. Furthermore, it allows scope for the *auctioning* of bands of frequencies within the bands shown, to operators for the purpose of providing services in different states, etc. Having bid for and won a piece of the spectrum, the service providers can introduce a technology which they see as best for the service that they have agreed to supply and which can be introduced in good time, with assurance.

Clearly any discussion of these aspects lies well outside the scope, or purpose, of this text, so we will just focus on three obvious opportunities:

1) PCS 1900 using D-AMPS principles
   This is exactly as described above (except for radio interface frequencies and channel numbers). The system comes as an upgraded IS-54 specification, known as IS-136, some features of which are described towards the end of Chapter 10.

2) PCS 1900 using DCS 1800 principles
   One now has DCS 1900, an exact replica of phase-2 GSM, i.e. fully feature rich. The methodology was fully described in Part 1 above.

3) PCS 1900 based on a CDMA technology

   One CDMA technology is fully defined under TIA/EIA standard IS-95. The air interface is based on the DS/SS operation; the exact specification is shown in Figure 8.12.

Part 3: Japanese digital cellular designs

9.4 JDC and PHS

9.4.1 Frequency availability

Japanese companies, particularly NTT, undertook the provision of cellular radio services in Japan, beginning with the analog JTACS service. This was very successful, so that, like the USA, in Japan they wished to introduce a backward compatible digital cellular, in the manner of D-AMPS. The real difference is the availability of frequencies, however.

Figure 9.27 shows the general World allocation of frequencies near 900 MHz. Like Figure 9.26 above, unfortunately, there exists a real incompatibility between the world radio regions. JDC, which is to take over from JTACS, now has two (small) bands at 800/900 and 1400 MHz. The former has a duplex separation of 130 MHz, the later a duplex separation of 48 MHz, both out of line with the systems described previously. Apart from this aspect, however, JDC comes very close to D-AMPS, in its operational characteristics. We will assume these features in general, except for the detailed differences to be now described.

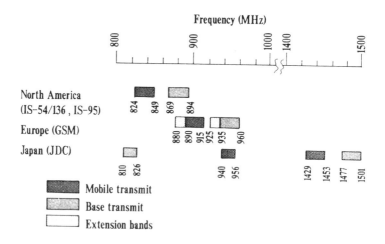

Figure 9.27 Regional and international wireless frequency allocations near 900 MHz

9.4.2 Air interface parameters

JTACS uses a 25 kHz channel plan (actually 50 kHz with interleaving). Likewise NTACS (like NAMPS) uses 25 kHz spacing, but which is then interleaved to give 12.5 kHz. Therefore JDC is based on a 25 kHz channel plan, which is then divided into three TDMA channels – like D-AMPS. Table 9.7 shows the air interface parameters for JDC, which should be compared to those of GSM (Table 9.3), and ADC (Table 9.6).

The bit transmission rte of 42 kbps is one of the lowest used, but since this is achieved in a 25 kHz bandwidth channel using $\pi/4$ DQPSK, this equivalent to a modulation efficiency of 1.68 bps/Hz, the most efficient of the three. Also, a comprehensive VSELP voice coding scheme working at 11.2 kbps, after coding, is again the most efficient. A desire to introduce spatial diversity at both the BS and MS is however evident. Like ADC, the JDC traffic time slot period contains no training period bits, as used in GSM. The number of traffic bits per TS is 112 + 112, i.e., smaller since the speech coding has a lower bit rate. Likewise, the control messages all have less bits, otherwise the JDC frame/time slot strategy is very similar to the diagram for ADC, i.e. Figure 9.21.

Table 9.7 The JDC air-interface parameters

Mobile to BS	810-826 MHz
	1477-1489 MHz
BS to mobile	940-956 MHz
	1429-1441 MHz
Channel spacing	25 kHz
R_x/T_x spacing – frequency	130/48 Mhz
R_x/T_x spacing – time	not known
Modulation	$\pi/4$ DQPSK
Users per frequency pair	3
Frame period	20 ms
Time slot period	6.667 ms
Bits period	23.8 µs
Bits/time slot	280 (including GS)
Transmission rate	42 kbps

9.4.3 Network configuration for JDC

The network architecture of JDC appears to differ extensively from the previous two TDMA digital standards. The network architecture is shown in Figure 9.28.

Apart from the rather different configuration and entity nomenclature, the real difference is that the JDC PLMN was from the beginning designed to support fixed *user parts* (UP), the existing PSTN and *packet switched public data network* (PSPDN), by means of an ISDN interface.

The network consists of the *mobile communications control centre*, the base station, and the mobile station. The MCC comprises three parts, which are logically independent of each other. They are a *gateway mobile communications control centre* (G-MCC), providing a toll switch function and gateway fixed network; a *visit mobile communications control centre* (V-MCC), providing location management and call connection functions; and an HLR, in which the mobile station numbers and areas where the subscribed belong are registered. A CCITT No 7 signalling system, which is a common channel signalling system separating the control signal path from the traffic path, is used for control signal transmission between control stations.

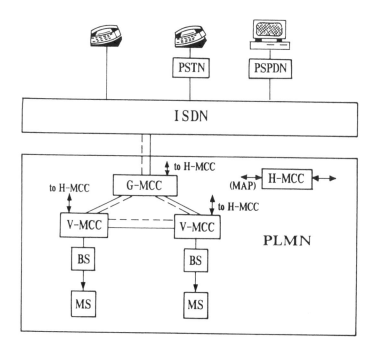

Figure 9.28 JDC network architecture outline

When the mobile station moves form its home cellular network to another part of the cellular network (roaming), it is necessary to track the connection between networks and to confirm that the roaming mobile station is an authentic user. To facilitate this connection tracking ability in the NTT system, a *gateway location register* (GLR) is provided to the HLR to temporarily store the data of a mobile station moving in from another network.

Where there is a call from a fixed telephone to this mobile station, the fixed network accesses the mobile station's HLR first and finds the cellular network, where the mobile station temporarily belongs. Then the fixed network accesses the GLR of that cellular network and finds the V-MCC, where the mobile station is located. The related MCC then pages the mobile.

This forward looking strategy adopted for the JDC network, with its direct interconnectivity with ISDN means that all the supplementary services of GSM phase 2 were in place from the outset.

9.4.4 The personal handyphone system (PHS)

It may seem rather strange to introduce what is known as a cordless telephone concept into the present discourse. One reason, however, is that the PHS technology is close to what has just been described in relation to JDC and ADC.

First of all, however, one can roughly differentiate cellular and cordless by looking at Table 9.8.

Table 9.8 Factors which distinguish cellular from cordless telephone operation

Factor	Cellular	Cordless
Cell size	generally large (0.5 -35 km)	small (50 - 500 m)
Movement of subscriber	could be up to 100 mph +	walking at the most
Coverage	large and continuous	very local and offices
MS complexity	high	low
MS battery	high power	low power
Channel plan	fixed by operator	should be flexible
BS deployment	complicated	many per zone
Subscription charge	set by operator	free, except for the call

Hopefully, this table shows that the so-called cordless technology is very attractive to people who want a wireless phone in their home, office, or various public concourses, but do not require the full service of cellular on a regional, national or international scale. There are now two TDMA technologies which provide this; they were introduced in Chapter 8. Their frequency assignments are to be found in Figure 9.26 above.

The PHS frame and time slot structure was shown in Figure 8.7. Table 9.9 gives the air-interface characteristics.

Table 9.9 Air-interface parameters of PHS

Frequency band	1895-1918.1 MHz
No of channels	37 Home/office 40 Public systems
Channel spacing	300 kHz
Voice coding	32 kbps ADPCM
Modulation	$\pi/4$ DQPSK
Carrier bit rate	384 kbps
Frame time	5 ms
Time slots	4 T_x, 4 R_x in TDD mode
Guard time	41.7 μsec
Control CH	Acts as beacon CH, followed by dynamic channel assignment
Handover	From synchronized BSs with MS assistance
MS power	Average 10 mW, with power control

The advantages of PHS (and the European counterpart described next) are the very low cost handsets (less technology and power deployed) and the lack subscription charges. They work as an attachment to the PSTN through very small stand-alone base stations, but do not require the cellular radio fixed supporting infrastructure. By virtue of the dedicated control channel, handover from BS to BS is obtainable. At the present time there are some one-third of a million base stations that give more or less seamless coverage in concourses, underground tube stations, etc., which would be expensive for cellular.

9.4.5 The European DECT system

DECT was introduced in Chapter 8, Figure 8.6, as a European digital cordless telephone development, based on the TDMA/TDD principle. It is now known as the *digitally enhanced cordless telecommunication* (DECT) system. Rather like GSM, the acronym remains the same, but the words changed, as the service attributes became more widely recognized.

It has features quite like PHS, and again has a specific allocation around 1.9 GHz, i.e. Figure 9.26. On the other hand it has a frame consisting of 24 time slots, 12 forward, 12 in reverse, for the *time division duplex* (TDD) mode of operation. Each time slot (Figure 8.6) has a good guard space equivalent to 56 b, which leaves the important 388 data bits free of any possible overlap. This data field is divided into an A-field (64 b for control) and a B-field (324 b for voice and data).

The main air-interface parameters of DECT are set out in Table 9.10.

Table 9.10 The air-interface parameters of DECT

Frequency allocation	1800-1900 MHz
No of channels	10, CHI=1881.792 MHz
Channel spacing	1.728 MHz
Frame duration	10 ms
No of time slots	12 + 12 (TDD)
Modulation	GFSK
Voice coding	32 kbps ADPCM
Bit rate	1152 kbps
Net rate in B-field	32 kbps
Peak RF power	250 mW
Mean RF power	10 mW

Like GSM, DECT has a much higher air-interface bit rate than the rate needed for voice alone. This over-reach, so to speak, can be put to important use, as in GSM, for a DECT handset can monitor and record the signal activity in adjacent channels, and cells, and create the opportunity to have *seamless* handover, i.e. use the A-field in the system. The handset actually requests the BS, or what is known as the *DECT radio fixed part* (RFP), to close down the first channel once the alternative is established.

The DECT system is based on an OSI layers structure, as is GSM, i.e. Table 9.1, and as a result GSM and DECT can be readily 'married' together. The easiest concept to illustrate this plan is Figure 9.29.

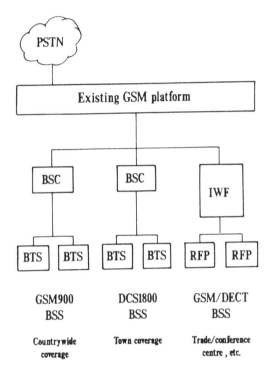

Figure 9.29 A concept of interworking between a GSM network and a DECT system attachment

The DECT RFP has a compatible A-interface output, the same as found behind a GSM BSC (Figure 9.4), provided that it is taken through an additional *interworking function* (IWF) unit. Therefore, as shown in Figure 9.29, one is able to achieve (using TDMA) a wireless telephony system which provides

- Wide/local coverage GSM
- Local/microcell DCS1800 coverage
- High capacity indoor office coverage with DECT

The PHS system is of course able to provide this very high density indoor coverage, but unfortunately the overlap of the earlier chosen frequencies of operation (Figure 9.26) could lead to operational and equipment design difficulties for dual, or multi-mode handsets, which are being developed.

DECT is also of interest to the cordless office application, because one can bundle the data 324 B-field bits together, over all twelve time slots per frame, and have a data rate potentially exceeding 100 kbps. At these high rates, multipath corruption, even inside a building must be not forgotten, however, since there is no training sequence correction mode within the DECT air-interface.

Further reading

Alcatel NV (1993). 'What are GSM and DCS', *Electrical Comms*, 2nd Quarter issue, pp 118-127

Alcatel NV (1993). 'DECT- cordless functionality in new generation PABX's', *Electrical Comms*, 2nd Quarter issue, pp 172-180

Balston, D.M. and Macario, R.C.V. (1993). *Cellular Radio Systems*, Artech House, Boston/London

Brydon, A.N. (1996). 'Cellular architectures and signalling', Chapter 6 in *Modern personal radio systems*, IEE Press, London

Calhoun, G. (1988). *Digital Cellular Radio*, Artech House, NY

D'Aria, G., Muratore, F. and Palestini, V. (1992). 'Simulator and performance of the pan-European land mobile radio system', *IEEE Trans Vech Tech*, VT-41, May, pp 177-189

Ericsson Radio Systems AB. (1991). *'Trends in Mobile Communications'*. Stockholm, Sweden

Ericsson Radio Systems AB. (1996), *D-AMPS: the smart way to go digital*, Stockholm, Sweden

Ericsson Radio Systems AB. (1996), *CMS 8800 – the dual-band system for PCS*, Texas, USA

Fernandes, V. (1996). 'Mobility handover and power control in GSM', Chapter 8 in *Modern personal radio systems*, IEE Press, London

Gardiner, J. and West, B. (1995). *Personal communication systems and technologies*, Artech House, Boston/London

Gibson, J.D. Ed, (1996). *The mobile communications handbook*, CRC Press, NY

Goodman, D.J. (1991). 'Second generation wireless information networks', *IEEE Trans Veh Tech,* VT- 40, May, pp 366-374

Hewlett-Packard Co (1992). *Communication Test Symposium – Digital RF Communications,* Feb, London, UK

Kinoshita, K., Kuramoto, M. and Nakajima, N. (1991). 'Development of TDMA Digital Cellular System based on Japanese Standard, *IEEE Veh Tech Conf,* May, pp 642–645

Lin, Y-B. and Chlamtac, I. (1996). 'Heterogeneous personal communication services; integration of PCS systems', *IEEE Communications*, Sept, pp 106-113

Motorola Ltd. (1992). *An Introduction to the Pan-European Digital Cellular Network,* European Cellular Infrastructure Division, Swindon, UK

Mouly, M. and Pautet, M-B. (1992). *The GSM system for mobile communications,* published by the authors, Paris

Mouly, M. and Pautet, M-B. (1995). 'Current evolution of the GSM system', *IEEE Personal Communications*, October, pp 9-19

Rappaport, T.S. (1996). *Wireless communications: principles and practice,* Prentice Hall, NY

Rohde & Schwarz UK Ltd. (1992). *Testing for GSM; Seminar notes,* April, London

Tuttlebee, W H W (1996), 'Cordless telephones and cellular radio : synergies of DECT and GSM', *Elec & Comms Eng J*, October, pp 213-223

10 Spectral Efficiency Considerations

10.1 Introduction

At the end of the day, whatever cellular radio system is considered, the following two factors will have to be taken into account:

(i)   The number of subscribers that can be connected to the system in an acceptable way for the radio spectrum allocated within a state or country desiring a cellular telephone service

and

(ii)   the initial and ongoing cost of the network to provide the number of subscribers contemplated, with a service of telephone quality.

The second factor is a subject of long and historic interest to telecommunication operators, but it is a subject somewhat outside the scope of this text. Indeed it is a matter fundamental to all public telephone operation, but academic textbooks on the matter appear to be scarce.

In early systems, much of the fixed network infrastructure was in existence for the fixed PSTN subscribers, and therefore the cellular network operator, having been granted a licence from the government or state to operate a cellular radio network, needed mainly to invest in:

Base stations and sites
Land lines (or microwave links) to switching centres
Mobile switching offices
Billing centre and invoice distribution
Network control centre
Management overhead (= staff)
Maintenance programmes

This assumes that the operator has access to long haul existing fixed network parts.

Notice that the cost of the mobile need not enter into the calculation, since provided that this can be kept low enough to attract subscribers, it need not concern the network operator.

Digital cellular radio is attractive because base station transmitters and receivers each serve several channels; eight in the case of GSM. Hence the network can be expanded at a lower cost, at least in principle.

Conversion equipment, from one speech coding method to another will be needed as described earlier, but otherwise much of the signalling, as opposed to traffic, can be common to the existing fixed network and the fixed part of the mobile network. Also there is more opportunity to reconfigure the network as traffic conditions change, by means of digital control. This situation is changing, however, as the cellular fixed network part suppliers produce complete stand-alone PLMN systems, with just the gateway entity parts connecting to the historically installed PSTN parts.

However, the matter of spectral efficiency is not reconfigurable. Once the limit marked as factor (i) above is reached, the subscriber base cannot be expanded and, more seriously, complaints of blocking or no line access and handover failures will arise. We review below the basics on which figures for spectral efficiency of cellular radio systems have been and are derived.

10.2 Bandwidth limit to subscribers

When it comes to towns or typical subscriber conurbations, cell layout plans as described in Chapter 3 initially would be used. It is useful to derive, therefore, a simple guide formula for the number of radio subscribers, in a province or city, who can expect to be offered a service at any particular time, on such a basis. For example, let

Area of the city being considered	$= A$ km^2
Population of the city	$= P$ thousands of people
Average radius of radio cell	$= R$ km (see Figure 1.6)
Number of radio channels in each cell	$= n_c$

n_c will depend on what cell repeat pattern is used and also on the spectrum allocated to the service. Cell patterns were described in Chapter 3; in particular Figure 3.13 will be useful, as will the associated discussion of channel allocation.

A radiotelephone system designed on a cellular basis also uses a dynamic assignment or trunking technique which can be interpreted as a channel gain, namely Figure 3.7, where, for example, typically 30 users think that they each have individual access to one private channel. Therefore, the number of users supported by each radio channel in the cell is multiplied by this factor.

We will use this factor of 30. It is convenient to approximate 30 as equal to the number 10π in the equation below.

$\therefore$ Number of users $\approx 30\ n_c \approx 10\pi n_c$

Meanwhile, number of cells in city $= \dfrac{A}{\pi R^2}$ (uniform cells)

$\therefore$ Total number of users supported $\approx 10\,\pi n_c \dfrac{A}{\pi R^2}$

As a percentage of number of population $= \dfrac{10 n_c A}{P \times 1000 \times R^2} \times 100$

or $\% = \dfrac{A n_c}{P R^2}$ (10.1)

Example

Consider a city of about half a million people, within a radius of six kilometres

$P \approx 500,000 = 500$
$A \approx 120\ \text{km}^2$
using $R = 2$ km   and $n_c = 40$

$\therefore$ % offered service $= \dfrac{120 \times 40}{500 \times 4} = 2.5\%$ of the population

The result shows that highly populated cities (A/P ratio small) are the most difficult to serve; also the cell size is critical, whilst one must maximize the number of channels in the allocated radio spectrum.

The result can, however, be rewritten involving the system allocated bandwidth ΔF, the effective channel bandwidth Δf_a, and cell cluster size N, because

$n_c = \dfrac{\Delta F}{\Delta f_a N}$ (10.2)

$\therefore$ $\% = \dfrac{A \Delta F}{P R^2 \Delta f_a N}$ (10.3)

This equation given previously as (6.3), shows that the success of cellular arrangement depends on the spectrum allocated per user, i.e. the term Δf_a, which, as was discussed above in section 6.2, is greater than the signal bandwidth Δf_m.

The result also shows that for dense subscriber scenarios, a good allocation of spectrum is needed, plus small cells and small cell clusters, where possible.

As Figure 3.13 showed, the term N does not reduce easily. A C/I hurdle has to be overcome. The TDMA technologies offer the opportunity of a reduction in N from 7 to 4, because of discontinuous transmission in the time frames, tight power control, and the voice quality threshold withstands a lower C/I ratio. On the other hand, a 4/12 cell pattern (Figure 3.21) does appear to be the norm.

10.3 Network example

Meanwhile, as an example, suppose one had the opportunity to consider setting up a cellular service where none existed, or indeed, which is unusual today, just a single private operator existed. Such an example is the small state of El Salvador in Central America. Figure 10.1 shows a map of the region as well as a geographical sketch of El Salvador.

The territory is interesting in the sense that it has many volcanic-like mountains or hills, which surround the main towns. Each main town has a population of well over 100,000 citizens, good connecting roads and enough vehicles to cause the usual traffic problems found almost anywhere. The present operator, TELEMOVIL El Salvador, S.A. offers an AMPS service, on the 333 A-channels shown in Figure 3.3, as clearly should be the case for a country in Region 2 of the World ITU regions, Figure 1.9. Assuming a 7-cell deployment (which could be sectored into a 7/21 cell plan), whose sites are mainly based on the hill top sites naturally available, this leaves at most, if the channels are equally employed among sites, (333-21)/7 or 44 channels per cell. This (by good fortune!) means that one could apply the example calculation given above for eqn (10.1), almost exactly. As the BS siting stands, however, quite large cells are implied (R > 2 km, according to the map), and an operator would be looking at deploying some 100/4 × 40/4 = 250 sites. Without very precise radiation pattern control, all the signals could be seen all over the state.

Another problem is one of the peak subscriber density in the main town centres and highways. A second operator using the B-channels on the same basis could not do much to solve the above problems.

As we shall see below, although digital cellular radio does not appear more efficient on a first pass calculation, it has so many deployment strategies that it can always be made to overtake analog cellular. For example, if a second service was introduced in our example country, by the resident PTT, ANTEL, in the B-AMPS channels, using D-AMPS (which gives 3 in place of 1 channel), then a 7/21 cell plan could be deployed using the same BS sites, but with a 3:1 cell size reduction, and more importantly, a 9:1 subscriber opportunity base improvement, i.e. eqn (10.1). Also, like GSM to DCS 1800, a D-AMPS to PCS 1900 network follow-through could be put into operation, with special emphasis on shopping centres, stadiums etc. Information on using the same operations support centre, home location registers, etc., for the two systems, whether the 800 MHz BS's or 1900 MHz BS's are located together, or separately is now generally available. The strategy is known as back-hauling.

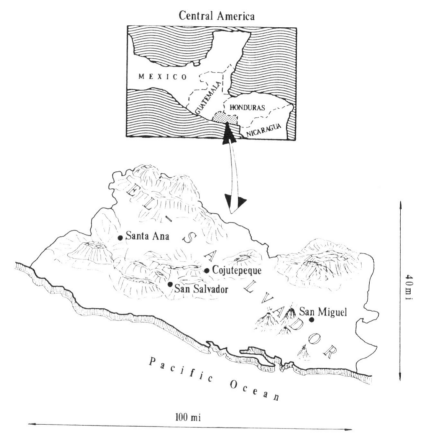

Figure 10.1 The region of Central America and a map of El Salvador in particular

10.4 Measures of spectral efficiency

Spectral efficiency for a land mobile radio system can be measured in two ways

(i)   Voice channels per MHz per km^2

The number of radio channels per MHz of spectrum bandwidth is most easily appreciated for an FDMA system, for example, Figure 3.1. The number of times that the same channels can be used in a given land area depends on the cluster arrangements.

This definition of spectral efficiency is easily calculated in general, since it is based on fully specified parameters, and we will proceed this way. However, spectral efficiency can also be defined in terms of the telephone traffic intensity, which can be supported by the network, giving the alternative definition

(ii)   Erlangs per MHz per km^2

This measures the quantity of traffic on a voice channel, or group of voice channels, per unit time. It is useful to recall the definition of traffic intensity here.

10.4.1 Definition of traffic intensity

The study of *traffic* is a well-established discipline in telephone systems. Note that the word traffic is not used to refer to the subscribers, even if they have radiotelephones.

Telephone calls are nearly always made by individual customers according to their living habit or more especially in the conduct of business. The aggregate of customers' calls follows a varying pattern throughout the day, and telephone facilities sufficient in quantity to provide for the period of maximum demand, called the *busy hour,* is a major aspect of PTT planning. The basic factors involved in the design of these facilities are the *call attempt rate, call-holding time, numbers of channels* (trunks or facilities), and *grade of service.*

The product of the first two factors is the *offered traffic.* It denotes the amount of time that a number of callers desire the use of facilities.

Thus, offered traffic = (attempt rate) × (call-holding time)

A load that engages one channel (trunk) completely all the time is known as an *Erlang* (defined below). Offered traffic is also expressed in terms of hundred call-seconds per hour (CCS), or call-minutes per hour.

Traffic flow through a switching centre is defined as the product of the number of calls during a period of time and their average duration. Traffic flow, therefore, can be expressed by the equation

traffic flow = (number of calls) × (mean call-holding time)

For example, if 100 calls of an average duration of three minutes are generated during a period of one hour, by subscribers connected to the input of an office or the local exchange, then the traffic flow for the group equals 300 call-minutes, or 5 call-hours.

10.4.2 *Erlangs and unit calls*

The international, dimensionless unit of telephone traffic is called the *Erlang*, named after a Danish telephone engineer, A.K. Erlang. One Erlang represents a circuit occupied for one hour; thus

$$1 \text{ Erlang} = 1 \text{ call-hour/hour} \tag{10.4}$$

The number of Erlangs per busy hour may be calculated as follows (call-holding time expressed in hours):

Erlangs = (calls/busy hour) × (mean call-holding time)

For example, consider a connection established at 9.00 am between a central computer and a data terminal. Assuming that the connection was maintained continuously and data was transferred at say, a rate of 1200 bps, determine the amount of traffic, in Erlangs, transferred over the established connection between 9.00 am and 9.45 am:

$\therefore$ Traffic = (1 call) (45 min) (= 0.75 hr) = 0.75 Erlangs

Note that the data rate is immaterial; the traffic is based solely on the call-holding time which, in this case, is 45 minutes or 0.75 hours.

When the call-holding time is expressed in seconds, the resulting traffic unit is the unit call or its synonymous terms: hundred-call-seconds or centum-call-seconds, (CCS), expressed as:

CCS = (calls/busy hour)(mean call-holding time)/100

Because there are 3600 seconds in an hour, the relationship between Erlangs and a hundred call-seconds pr hour (CCS), is

$$1 \text{ Erlang} = 36 \text{ CCS} \tag{10.5}$$

CCS is the traffic unit employed mainly in North America, but traffic expressed in Erlangs is generally more useful and provides direct information about the traffic, i.e.

- The Erlangs per channel represents its efficiency; that is, the proportion of the hour during which the channel is occupied.

- Traffic expressed in Erlangs designates the average number of calls in progress simultaneously during a period of one hour.
- Erlang figures represent the total time, expressed in hours, to carry all calls.

For example, if a group of 30 trunks are required to carry 12 Erlangs of traffic during the busy hour, what is the efficiency of this trunk group?

Since,   12 Erlangs/30 trunks = 0.40 Erlangs per trunk
   ∴ Trunk-group efficiency = 0.40 = 40%

10.5 Grade of service

Grade of service (GOS) is a measure of the probability that a percentage of the offered traffic will be blocked or delayed and therefore the aim is to make the GOS = 0. Grade of service, therefore, involves not only the ability of a system to interconnect subscribers, but the rapidity with which the interconnections are made. As such, grade of service is commonly expressed as the fraction of calls, or demands, that fail to receive immediate service (blocked calls), or the fraction of calls that are forced to wait longer than a given time for service (delayed calls).

The assessment of the grade of service provided to the user, and the determination of facilities required to provide a desirable grade of service, are based on mathematical formulas derived from statistics and the laws of probability. If a system is engineered on the basis of the fraction of calls blocked, then it is said to be engineered on a blocking basis. Blocking can occur if all facilities are occupied when a demand is originated or, in the case where several facilities must simultaneously be connected, a matching of idle facilities cannot be made even, though only certain facilities are idle in each group. Some areas where engineering is done on the basis of blocking criteria are the dimensioning of space switches and inter-office trunk groups. Another basis for setting a service standard is to have a fraction of calls delayed longer than an acceptable time, before setting up. The delay encountered in providing a voice channel after accessing a control channel for a subscriber is an example. As the number of common-control and time-sharing systems increases, so does the need for engineering on a delay basis.

10.5.1 Telephone traffic formulas

The assumption, blocked calls cleared, is the basis of a formula for obtaining the probability of loss, known as the *Erlang B* formula. The alternative is for some calls, upon finding no channel available, to wait until one becomes idle, at which time the channel is seized and then held for the full holding time. This assumption, *blocked calls delayed*, is the basis of the *Erlang C* formula. Between these extremes is an intermediate assumption called *blocked calls held*, which are the basis of the so-called *binomial* and *Poisson* formulas. In this last case an offered call, upon finding no channel idle, waits for an interval of time exactly equal to its holding time and then disappears from the system. If a trunk becomes idle while the call is waiting, the trunk is seized and occupied for the portion of the holding time remaining. This is known as the lost-calls-held assumption to distinguish it from the other assumptions used in the Erlang formulas. We shall not discuss any of these formulas here, except to note that a mobile radiotelephone service is often closely described by the blocked-calls-cleared (Erlang B) formula when considering the voice channels.

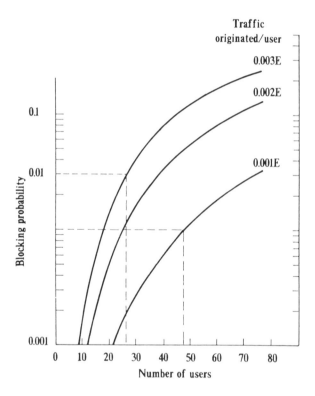

Figure 10.2   The probability of a cell being denied (blocked) in a three channel trunked system versus the number of users offering low calling rates (in Erlangs)

Nevertheless, it needs to be noted that for the control channels (in an FDMA arrangement) a different situation applies. Firstly, the messages (signalling) are very short, there is only a finite number of subscribers in a cell, and any blocked calls are cleared. An alternative traffic formula known as the *Engset* formula applies. Figure 10.2 show the result of calculating the likelihood of blocking (blocking probability) versus the offered traffic (Erlangs) for a three channel scheme. One notes how many more users than control channels can be accepted, and in most cases any control channel restriction is transparent to a subscriber.

However, with regard to the voice or message channel the subscribers are likely to be making long calls, i.e. of the order of minutes. In a large cell the traffic could amount to several Erlangs. As an example, the Erlang B formula is applied to find the offered traffic which meets a specified grade of service in a group of n channels.

10.5.2 Activity in a cell

Tables of results of the Erlang B formula, which list the grade of service applicable for an offered traffic with n voice channels, are given for example in the book by J R Boucher, referenced as further reading on this subject.

Firstly, we need to agree on some average calling rate for a subscriber and his holding time. Typical figures are six calls a day of 150 sec (2.5 min) duration. Hence traffic flow per subscriber is

$$\frac{6 \times 150}{60 \times 60 \times 24} = 0.0104 \text{ Erlangs}$$

Because our subscriber is unlikely to be operating over a 24-hour day, his traffic flow will tend to bunch up and the more likely traffic generated during the *busy hour* is, say, 0.03 Erlangs.

In any given cell we will have many (average) subscribers. How many is determined by the traffic capacity of the cell, or base station, assuming n_c channels and a certain grade of service, determined by the Erlang B formula; therefore

$$\text{No. of subscribers per cell (BS)} = \frac{\text{traffic capacity of base station}}{\text{calling rate of subscriber}} \quad (10.6)$$

Table 10.1 lists the traffic capacity of a cell for a grade of service equal to 0.01, for the channel numbers n_c, which were listed in Table 3.1, for a 300 channel network.

Table 10.1 Traffic capacity data for TACS type cellular plan (using data in Table 3.1) and GOS = 0.01

Cluster size N	No. of channels n_c	(a) Offered traffic GOS = 0.01	(b) No. of Subscribers per cell	(c) No. of Subscribers per CH
3	93	77.2	2583	28
4	69	55.2	1840	27
7	39	28.1	937	24
9	31	21.2	707	23
12	23	14.5	483	21

(a) from Erlang B table

(b) from (10.6)

(c) column (b) divided by n_c

Note that column (b) is the one shown as column (d) in Table 3.1. The interesting feature of the table, however, is that the number of subscribers per channel does not change very much with cluster size, when keeping GOS constant; in fact the figure of 30 used in eqn (10.1) is quite a reasonable approximation. The benefit of a small cluster size, n, is the minimization of handover activities in a given cluster area.

Figure 10.3 illustrates further data for alternative grades of service and offered traffic (in Erlangs). The curves are worked out using Erlang B tables and (10.6), namely

$$\frac{\text{Subscribers}}{\text{per channel}} = \frac{\text{Traffic cap. of BS} = n_c \text{ (assuming GOS} = 0.01)}{\text{Subscriber Erlang rate assumed} = 0.03} \times \frac{1}{n_c} \quad (10.7)$$

Cells with only a few channels can only handle a few subscribers; too many channels per BS has no clear benefits either. On the other hand, from a spectral efficiency viewpoint, it is clear that a measurement based on voice channels, definition (i), is a more precise definition.

10.6 Calculation of spectral efficiency

The definition: Channels per MHz per km² implies

$$\eta_s = \frac{\text{total number of channels available}}{\text{total BW available} \times \text{cluster area}} \quad (10.8)$$

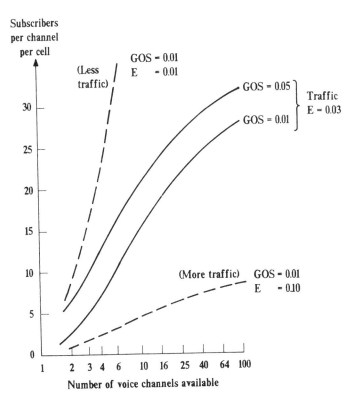

Figure 10.3 The subscribers per channel per cell versus the total number of voice channels per cell for specific grades of service

Assuming a uniform cellular layout arrangement consisting of clusters of N cells, each cell of which occupies an area S, and since

total BW available $= N \times n_c \times f_s$

where f_s is the bandwidth assigned to each subscriber

$$\therefore \eta_s = \frac{n_c}{BWS} = \frac{1}{f_s NS} \tag{10.9}$$

This result indicates that narrowband (or low bit rate) technologies are best, small cluster sizes N are desirable, together with small cells. Note that, though η_s is termed an efficiency, in reality, it is a number much greater than one, being the number of voice channels per MHz of allocated spectrum over the ground area being served.

10.6.1 Conventional cellular cells

Here f_s refers to an individual voice channel, whether digital or analog modulation. In the digital case, we write

$$f_s = \frac{f_b}{mK} + 2\Delta f \qquad (10.10)$$

here f_b = voice coding bit rate
  m = modulation efficiency
  K = FEC rate as a fraction < 1
  Δf = hardware frequency error.

To minimize f_s need low f_b
  m high
  $K = 1$
  Δf minimum

f_b and m were discussed in Chapter 6. For GMSK, measurement of the 60 dB adjacent channel performance shows that with BT = 0.3, $m \approx 1.35$; which implies a 16 kHz channel needed for 22 kbps speech, which also allows for the code correction bits.

Alternatively, $\pi/4$ DPSK offers $m \approx 1.62$, which allows 48 kbps in 30 kHz, which is why it is successful for D-AMPS.

Turning to cluster size N, the co-channel interference dependence was introduced in Chapter 3. Recalling (3.1), i.e.

$$N = \frac{1}{3}\left(\frac{D}{R}\right)^2$$

where R = cell radius and D = reuse distance, we found that the carrier-to-co-channel interference ratio C_i could be written as

$$C_i = 1.5N^2 \qquad (10.11)$$

assuming an inverse fourth power propagation law. More precise calculations of C_i versus N are possible, but do not affect the results below significantly. It is perhaps worth noting that whatever the cluster size, the number of interferers can remain equal to six, i.e. see Figure 10.4.

Therefore as a reasonable approximation we can write, by combining the results

$$\eta_s = \frac{mK}{f_b} \times \left(\frac{3}{2C_i}\right)^{\frac{1}{2}} \times \frac{1}{S} \tag{10.12}$$

where $\Delta f \to 0$, which is generally true for digital cellular.

As a further helpful approximation, let the factor mK balance out the number root 3/2, and since $S = \pi R^2$, where R = cell radius,

$$\therefore \ \eta_s = \frac{1}{f_b} \times \frac{1}{(C_i)^{\frac{1}{2}}} \times \frac{1}{\pi R^2} \tag{10.13}$$

The result is interesting in the sense that it is the carrier-to-cochannel interference ratio which should be minimized, and to some extent the number of cells in a cluster is immaterial, which indeed is now current practice.

The other factor which must be kept in mind, however, is the relation between the FEC and C_i ratio, since more correction may be needed to sustain a lower C_i ratio. The whole matter is complicated by the fading statistics of the wanted and interfering signals.

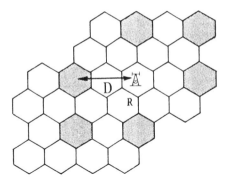

Figure 10.4 A cluster size of N = 4, showing the six interfering cells

10.7 Multi-access efficiency factor

Provided that the channels discussed above can be fully loaded with voice traffic, then the efficiency, in Erlangs per MHz per km², is almost equal to the factor η_s above. To load up each channel a multi-access scheme must be employed, and one assumes that there are many more users than channels. How efficient is this *access* facility? One approach is to multiply η_s by a term η_a, where

$$\eta_a = \frac{\text{Total time / bandwidth product devoted to the voice channels}}{\text{Total time / bandwidth product devoted to the system}} \quad (10.14)$$

∴ overall efficiency $\eta_o = \eta_s \times \eta_a$ discussed further below.

For *FDMA*, this has been discussed in section 6.2 in relation to the need for guard bands between channels, and also the need for control channels in the arrangement, see Figure 4.2.

Clearly $\eta_a \leq 1$

For *TDMA*, the efficiency will depend on how many bits in a time frame are dedicated to the message and how many are overhead. In narrowband TDMA systems, an FDMA breakup of the available spectrum also exists, see Figure 8.2. For one TDMA channel group, it follows that

$$\eta_a = \frac{(\text{time slot duration for voice}) \times N_F}{\text{frame duration}} \quad 10.15)$$

where

N_F = no. of time slots for voice transmission per frame.

To work out the access efficiency using bit numbers and equation (10.15) requires taking out the parts of the message used for forward error correction etc., but in the first instance, let

t_s = time slot duration of the message
T_F = frame duration

$$\therefore \eta_a = \frac{t_s \times N_F}{T_F} \quad (10.16)$$

If one takes GSM (Chapter 9, Table 9.3) as an example, then we have

Time slot period   = 576.9 μs
Frame period   = 4.615 ms
No. of users per frame = 8

Hence $\eta_a = \dfrac{0.5769 \times 8}{4.615} = 1.0$, or 100%

Unfortunately, much of each time slot is taken up with error protection bits, tail bits, training sequence and a guard space, so that a more accurate indication of the access efficiency comes from the alternate formula

$$\eta_a = \frac{(\text{voice channel bps}) \times N_F}{(\text{group bandwidth bps})} \qquad (10.17)$$

Again taking GSM as an example, and using (10.17) we have

voice channel bit rate	= 13 kbps
group bandwidth bit rate	= 270.833 kbps
No of channels per frame	= 8

$$\therefore \eta_a = \frac{13 \times 8}{271} = 0.38, \text{ or } 38\%$$

As an alternative, one could consider D-AMPS (Chapter 9, Table 9.6); we have

voice channel bit rate	= 7.95 kbps
group bandwidth bit rate	= 48.6 kbps
No of channels per frame	= 3

$$\therefore \eta_a = \frac{7.95 \times 3}{48.6} = 0.49, \text{ or } 49\%$$

There is an improvement in access efficiency over GSM by something like 29%, but not orders of magnitude, if one just looks at the time slot plans for the two TDMA standards. The improved channel capacity of D-AMPS (ADC) noted earlier in Table 8.1 is a result of both the access efficiency and the spectral efficiency.

For narrowband TDMA, as explained, more spectrum is available in the other channel groups on an FDMA principle. Therefore, the access efficiency must also be modified by the term

$$\eta'_a = \frac{(\text{bandwidth for a frame}) \times \text{no. of bands}}{(\text{total BW of system})} \qquad (10.18)$$

Let bandwidth per frame	= B_f
no. of radio bands	= N_c

$$\therefore \eta'_a = \frac{B_f \times N_c}{BW} \qquad (10.19)$$

In the primary GSM band, $B_f = 200$ kHz, $N_c = 50$ and BW = 10 MHz

$$\therefore \eta'_a = \frac{200 \times 50}{10,000} = 1$$

so no efficiency is lost through the narrowband TDMA format plan.

In TACS, $B_f = 25$ kHz, $N_c = 1000$, for a BW = 25 MHz, so the access efficiency would appear to be unity. As we know several channels are allocated to control channels between the different operators, so the access efficiency is actually less than unity, i.e. at best by the ratio $(1000 - 42)/1000$.

10.7.1 Overall efficiency

The overall efficiency is the product of spectral efficiency and access efficiency i.e.

$$\eta_o = \eta_s \times \eta_a \qquad\qquad (10.20)$$

Because, as we found, η_a could effectively be engineered to be one hundred per cent, we could accept that the overall efficiency, i.e. the number of voice channels as discussed after equation (10.9), is determined by

$$\eta_s$$

which is decided by the terms in equation (10.13).

The formula for η_s however, it will be recalled, is an approximation; it hides the loss of performance due to FEC. Also, in the case of narrowband TDMA the access efficiency is not unity, again due to all the overheads in the speech coding algorithm, the time slot and the frame itself, and appears to represent quite a serious loss of efficiency. However, the speech coding provides transmission security by optional levels of encryption and therefore represents additional service over and above plain speech. Nevertheless, the basic formula for η_s indicates the real limits of cellular radio. These are

(i)   the voice communication bandwidth or bit rate. Here digital technology of high quality is now drawing level with analog. (We have not referred to what is known as *half-rate speech coding* in this text. This is, or was, a plan to introduce speech codecs which would work with half the number of bits per segment. This would allow, for example, the number of time slots in a frame to be doubled, i.e. twice the traffic could be supported by each frequency at a BS, with a consequential very large leap in the traffic capability in Erlangs. It has been found that the loss of quality and likelihood of threshold failure does not warrant half-rate coding as a good marketing planning strategy. The techniques described in the next section have greater operator appeal.)

(ii) the tolerable carrier to co-channel interference. A 6 dB change here can represent a 40% improvement in efficiency. The technique here is to move away from conventional cell cluster designs, as we shall examine in the next section.

(iii) Any minimizing of the cell size will show real benefit. Power control of the base station and mobile transmitter by digital control makes for smaller cell geometry. The concept of picocell, microcell and a macrocell hierarchy has come into place.

Using TDMA avoids the problem of equipment centre frequency drift as compared to narrowband FDMA technology, but as the bit rate per channel is increased more irreducible BER is encountered on the radio path due to multipath.

This irreducible BER is due to intersymbol interference (ISI) caused by multipath delay spread **s**. Experience has shown that ISI becomes noticeable when

Signal bit rate $<$ 10 **s** (10.21)

In the case of the ADC (and JDC) systems we have $T_b = 1/48600 = 20.5$ µs, which is about ten times the average delay spread. For GSM, on the other hand, the signalling rate is 271 kbps, corresponding to a symbol period of 3.7 ms, which comes much closer to a delay spread value of say 2 µs. This is why 26 bits need to be dedicated to an in the time slot training period within the GSM frame format. Therefore, some of the efficiency of a wider band TDMA format has to be given over to extra overhead within the signalling, as was found above.

10.8 Optimization strategies

10.8.1 Macrocell operation

Figure 10.5 shows a more realistic portrayal of our radio cell. Whereas it was indicated right at the beginning of the text, radio cells have somewhat ill-defined boundaries, i.e. Figure 1.5, as is customary, one can proceed quite well despite this and build up clusters, etc. Cells of course can be numbered, i.e. Figure 9.16. The roughness of the cell boundary is not really the problem however; handover strategies can manage this. The problem areas are those highlighted in Figure 10.4:

- blind spots - due to shadowing, tunnels, etc
- regions of likelihood of deep fades in signal level

Blind spots can be overcome by the use of *on-frequency-repeaters*. This is a unit which receives a signal selectively in one direction, amplifies it, and then reradiates an exact replica in the opposite direction. Clearly the signal level received should be above the acceptable MS threshold, while the signal re-radiated needs to be below the forward-back gain ratio of the repeater antenna to prevent self-oscillation. Applying, for example, a 25 dB step of signal level to, say, the curves in Figure 2.11, would move the cell coverage out by nearly two times, or more importantly, radiate into a blind spot. The repeater station clearly has to be bi-directional, since a MS in a blind spot also needs to be able to get its signals back to base. Therefore, the repeater's aim is not to extend the boundaries of a cell, but to lift the signal out of the shadow regions, depicted in Figure 10.5, and set it to the level it should have been, but for the shadowing. The repeaters can be of three types

    broadband repeaters
    band selective repeaters
    channel selective repeaters

The last type are of greatest interest, since they do not add to the ACI, but are tuned selectively to the *donor* BS channels. The channels filters can be remotely tuned if need be. In a tunnel, the repeater output antenna could be replaced by a leaky feeder arrangement, is another alternative.

For regions, particularly associated with macrocells, only a few scattered signals are present, e.g. Figure 2.6. The signal envelope can then go through a deep null, as explained by Figure 5.4. This null can be particularly disastrous for a pedestrian user, for example, as he will arrive at a null (the star points shown in Figure 10.5) and he will lose service. This is a bad scene as far as a customer/operator setup is concerned, yet is very difficult to guard against. (Analog cellular is less affected because the user can hear the fade and moves accordingly.) Also within the cell, handover may not be practical unless a cell overlay plan has been put into operation as discussed in the next section.

The answer is to use frequency hopping as previously explained in section 5.4, and Figure 5.14; also known as frequency diversity.

Frequency hopping requires a set of frequencies distributed *over all sites*. For primary band GSM, there are only a maximum of 50 frequencies (channels) available, divided between two operators, into 4/3, = 12 cell clusters, which means only two frequencies per cell, i.e. Figure 3.21. In GSM, the specification says the sequences of frequencies should go from the lowest frequency in a group to the highest, and then start again.

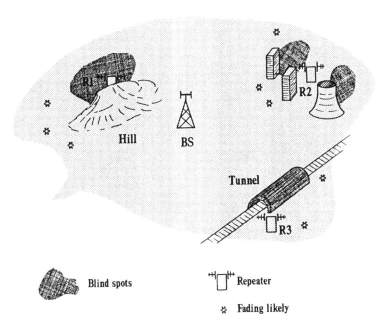

Figure 10.5   A possible macrocell serviced by a single base station, and the likely places of service difficulty

As more frequencies become available, i.e. Figure 3.4, other hopping sequences over larger number of ARFCH's are possible. In particular an *orthogonal* frequency set ensures that the same time slots do not use the same frequencies at the same time. With all these schemes *interference averaging* is automatically achieved, i.e. any interference tends to be spread around, as well as the removal of dropped-call spots.

10.8.2 Hierarchical cell plans

Figure 10.6 shows another typical cellular radio environment scenario, i.e. a business park, a city complex, University campus, etc. A macrocell would give overall area coverage, and take command of traffic motoring past. A microcell area is shown which would focus on slow moving subscribers moving between high-rise buildings, for example; while a picocell focuses on the foyer of a theatre, or exhibition centre, etc.

The plan therefore is to have

			cell layer
←	MACROCELLS	→	3
← microcells	– microcells	→	2
← picocells	– picocells	→	1

The functionality of the lower layers is to provide capacity, whilst the function of the upper layer (3) is to provide coverage, over the gaps in the lower layers.

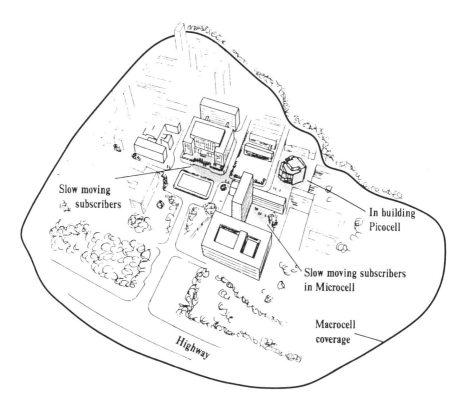

Figure 10.6   Conceptual view of a subscriber area which has an overlaid/underlaid cell plan – see text

A subscriber moving into the region would be operating in a macrocell plan, no doubt laid out on a 4/12 cell plan. These are known as *underlaid* cells, one of which is shown in Figure 10.6 If he was just moving through he would stay on his macrocell channel, handing over to the next cell in that layer further away. On entering a hierarchical cell environment, however, he would be handed down to a lower layer cell as soon as the network received suitable confirmation. The subscriber could then work in a cell plan with all the extra channels, except those of the single macrocell. For a subscriber opening up in the multi-layer environment, priority of cell use is given to the lower layers, i.e. the picocells, if available, which can handle the most MS's. As the MS moved about he could be assigned between layers, mainly the lower two layers, only going to layer 3 if he moved out of coverage of what is termed, the *overlaid* cells. GSM and D-AMPS phones have the ability to scan all the frequencies and time slots, and organize TS to TS and intra-cell handover. It will therefore be appreciated that these digital technologies can increase the subscriber density base far beyond that conceived for simple cell cluster structures.

Further reading

Boucher, N.J. (1990). *Cellular Radio Handbook,* Quantum Publishing Inc, USA

Boucher, J.R. (1988). *Voice Teletraffic Systems Engineering,* Artech House Inc, USA

Chia, S.T.S. (1996). 'Design and optimisation for cellular access network', *Elec. & Comms Eng J*, December

Chuang, J.C.I. (1989). 'The effects of delay spread on 2-PSK, 4. PSK, 8-PSK, and 16- QAM in a portable radio environment', *IEEE Trans Veh Tech,* Vol 38, May, pp 43-45

Dahlin, J. (1996), 'Ericssons's multiple reuse pattern for DCS1800', *Mobile Communications International*, November

Dornstetter, J-L and Verhulst, D. (1987) 'Cellular efficiency with slow frequency hopping: analysis of the digital SFH 900 mobile system', *IEEE Select Areas Comms* Vol 5, June, pp 835-848

Ericsson Radio Systems AB (1996), 'D-AMPS; the smart way to go digital, Brochure no EZ/LZT/ 123 3172

Farr, R.E. (1988). *Telecommunications Traffic, Tariff and Costs*, Peter Peregrinus, IEE Press, UK

Gill, T.M. (1993). 'An automated system for frequency planning of cellular radio networks', *IEE Conference on Telecommunications*, Manchester, April

Haas, R. and Belfiore, J-C, (1996). 'Spectrum efficiency limits in mobile cellular systems', *IEEE Trans Veh Tech* Vol 45, Feb, pp 33-40

Hatfield, D.N. (1977). 'Measures of spectral efficiency in land mobile radio', *IEEE Trans EMC,* Vol 19, Aug, pp 266-8

Hummuda, H., McGeeham, J.P. and Bateman, A. (1988). 'Spectral efficiency of cellular land mobile radio systems', *IEEE Veh Tech Conference no 38,* pp 616-22

Lee, W.C.Y. (1989). 'Spectrum efficiency in cellular', *IEEE Trans Veh Tech,* Vol 38, May, pp 69-75

Motorola Inc. (1996), 'Cellular communications – the shape of things to come', *Mobile Communications International,* March

Murota, K. (1985). 'Spectrum efficiency of GMSK land mobile radio', *IEEE Trans Veh Tech,* Vol 34, May, pp 69-75

Nokia Telecommunications Ltd (1996). 'Capacity increase in cellular radio networks using existing base station sites', *IEE Colloquia: Propagation aspects for future mobile systems,* London, October

Pollini, G.P. (1996). 'Trends in handover design', *IEEE Comms Magazine,* March, pp 82-90

Raith, K. and Uddenfeldt, J. (1991). 'Capacity of digital cellular TDMA systems', *IEEE Trans Veh Tech,* Vol 40, May, pp 323-31

Appendix I Cellular Radio Systems

List of the principal cellular radio systems found today

NMT	Nordic mobile telephone (followed by a number referring to the frequency band)
AMPS	Advanced mobile phone system (USA)
TACS	Total access communication systems (UK)
E-TACS	Extended TACS, offering more channels by additional frequency assignment
GSM	Global system for mobile communications – specified by CEPT (Committee of European Posts and Telecommunications)
JTACS	Japanese total access communications system, similar to TACS
JDC	Japanese digital cellular; a narrowband TDMA system
ADC	American digital cellular (similar to JDC; works within the AMPS frequency plan)
N-AMPS	Narrowband version of AMPS
D-AMPS	New name for ADC, i.e. digital AMPS
DCS 1800	GSM system operating at 1800 MHz
PCS 1900	The DCS 1800 system, or D-AMPS system at 1900 MHz in the Americas
PHS	Japanese PCS system, known as personal handy-phone system; operates at 1900 MHz
DECT	Digitally enhanced cordless telecommunication; operates at 1800 Mhz

Appendix II Telecommunication Services

Services available in GSM phase 2

TELESERVICES (i.e. applications of underlying bearer services)
Telephony
Emergency Calls for SIM-less mobiles
Short Message Service Point to Point Mobile Terminated
Short Message Service Point to Point Mobile Originated
Short Message Service Cell Broadcast
Automatic Fax Group 3
BEARER SERVICES (i.e. communication capabilities)
Full-rate speech (13 kbps coding)
Half-rate speech (7 kbps coding)
Circuit switched data (asynchronous) at 300,1200,1200/75,2400,4800,9600 bps
Circuit switched data (synchronous) at 1200,2400,4800,9600 bps
PAD access (asynchronous) at 300,1200,1200/75,2400,4800,9600 bps
Packet network access (synchronous) at 1200,2400,4800,9600 bps
Alternate speech and data (asynchronous) at 300,1200,2400,4800,9600,1200/75 bps
Speech followed by data (asynchronous) at 300,1200,2400,4800,9600,1200/75 bps
SUPPLEMENTARY SERVICES (i.e. enhancements)
Call forwarding unconditional
Call forwarding on mobile subscriber not reachable
Call forwarding on mobile subscriber busy
Call forwarding on no reply
Barring of all outgoing calls
Barring of all outgoing international calls
Barring of all outgoing international calls except to home PLMN country
Barring of all incoming calls
Barring of incoming calls when roaming outside home PLMN country
Calling Line Identity Presentation
Calling Line Identity Restriction
Connected Line Identity Presentation
Connected Line Identity Restrictions
Call Waiting
Call Hold
Call Transfer
Multi-Party service
Closed User Group
Advice of Charge - Information
Advice of Charge - Charging
Unstructured Supplementary Service Data

Services under development in GSM phase 2+

Call Deflection
Call Forward Enhancements
Completion of Calls to Busy Subscriber i.e. Ring Back When Free
Completion of Calls to subscriber when No Reply
Completion of Calls when subscriber Not Reachable
Compression of user data
DECT access to GSM networks
Direct Subscriber Access and Restriction
Explicit Call Transfer
Facsimile enhancements
General Packet Radio Service
High speed circuit switched data i.e. data rates > 9.6 kbps
Location services
Malicious Call Identification
Mobile Access Hunting
New Barring Services
Packet data on GSM signalling channels
Payphone services
Premium rate services
Proactive SIM
Support of operator specific services when roaming
Support of optimal routing
Support of Private Numbering Plan

Note: Many, or most, of these services can also be found on D-AMPS and JDC
networks.

Index